'Annie, you ⟨...⟩
Marc bega⟨n⟩

'I tell you I've never been there. Never in this life,' Annie replied.

There was an odd, echoing silence.

His voice low, he murmured, 'Never in this life, no, Annie—but you have been there and you're starting to remember. You've started following a path I've already been along. What you dreamt about now really happened, you see. I have dreamt that for years now. I remember every tiny detail, with very good reason. That's how I died.'

Dear Reader

Summer is here at last...! And what better way to enjoy these long, long days and warm romantic evenings than in the company of a gorgeous Mills & Boon hero? Even if you can't jet away to an unknown destination with the man of your dreams, our authors can take you there through the power of their storytelling. So pour yourself a long, cool drink, relax, and let your imagination take flight...

The Editor

Charlotte Lamb was born in London in time for World War II, and spent most of the war moving from relative to relative to escape bombing. Educated at a convent, she married a journalist, and now has five children. The family lives in the Isle of Man. Charlotte Lamb has written over a hundred books, most of them for Mills & Boon.

Recent titles by the same author:

FALLING IN LOVE
WOUNDS OF PASSION
BODY AND SOUL
VAMPIRE LOVER

DYING
FOR YOU

BY
CHARLOTTE LAMB

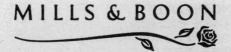

MILLS & BOON

MILLS & BOON LIMITED
ETON HOUSE, 18-24 PARADISE ROAD
RICHMOND, SURREY TW9 1SR

*MILLS & BOON and the Rose Device
are trademarks of the publisher.*

*First published in Great Britain 1994
by Mills & Boon Limited*

© Charlotte Lamb 1994

*Australian copyright 1994   Philippine copyright 1994
This edition 1994*

ISBN 0 263 78573 4

*Set in Times Roman 10 on 12 pt.
01-9408-52891 C*

Made and printed in Great Britain

CHAPTER ONE

ANNIE got the first phone call at midnight on a cold spring night.

'Remember me?' a voice whispered, and the hairs on the back of her neck stood up.

She had only just got back to her London flat, she was alone, and already on the verge of tears because her best friend, Diana, had just married the man Annie loved.

'Who is this?' she asked, then wondered if it was one of the band, who were all still drinking at the bar in the hotel where the wedding reception had been held. When they were drunk all five of them could do the silliest things.

But there was no reply. The phone went dead. She hung up, frowning, then switched on the answering machine. The last thing she needed tonight was crank phone calls.

She turned away with a swish of silk, comforted by the sensual feel of the sleek material against her skin. Annie loved good clothes. She had helped Diana choose her wedding-dress and had chosen the dress she herself wore as bridesmaid—almond-green silk, a colour which exactly matched the colour of her eyes. She would be able to wear it for parties afterwards. There was a faintly Victorian look about the style of the dress, as there had been about Di's wedding-dress; and Annie had put up her long black hair into a smooth chignon at the back of her head, carried a tiny Victorian-style bouquet of violets displayed on ferns.

She must take the best-looking flower and a spray of fern out of the bouquet, and put them between the pages of a book of poetry. She often pressed wild flowers in books; she liked finding them when she turned the pages years afterwards, being reminded of some special day, some important moment in her life. They always seemed to retain their scent, yet altered and nostalgic, a gentle, faded sweetness that gave her back instant memories.

However hurt she felt, she knew this had been a very important day in her life; she would want to remember it.

Yawning, she looked at her watch. Bed! she thought, seeing that it was way past midnight now. Annie kept strict hours when she wasn't performing on stage. She would be in bed by ten most days, up very early, and tomorrow was no different. Tomorrow she had to be up at seven. She had a photo call at nine at the recording studio where she was just putting the final touches to her new disc.

She took off her green silk dress and hung it up carefully in her wall-to-wall wardrobe, put on a brief nightdress and matching négligé, then sat down at the dressing-table and started to take off her make-up, and smooth a toning lotion into her skin. However late, however tired she was, Annie always went through the same routine before going to bed.

'When you're in the public eye all the time people notice everything about you, so never forget to look your best. You are always going to be on stage!' Philip had told her years ago.

She hadn't been sure then that she liked the idea. In fact, it had been her first premonition that fame and success were not going to be without their drawbacks.

Philip had watched her shrewdly. 'Not so sure you like that, kid? Well, now's the time to make your mind up, before you really get started. If you want to be a star you have to take the rough with the smooth; there's no two ways about it. If you want out now, you only have to say so. Nobody knows you yet; you can easily go back to your old life without anyone being any the wiser.'

She hadn't wanted out. She had looked at him with wide, melancholy green eyes and sighed.

'There's nothing for me to go back to,' she remembered saying. 'I want to be a singer more than anything else in the world.'

It had been that simple then; it was that simple now, and yet it got harder every year, although that was something Philip hadn't warned her about. The strain of being at the top and fighting to stay there was only a part of it; there was a more personal price to pay, because the public wouldn't give you any space. They ate you up if you let them, and you never knew whether you could trust the people you met; you couldn't be sure if they really liked you, or were starstruck, or wanted to use you in some way.

That was a hard lesson to learn. It hurt, and you were tempted to grow a second skin, toughen up; but Annie instinctively knew you couldn't let yourself get too tough or the music would lose something vital. Getting hurt sometimes seemed essential to the music. Some of her best songs had been written about her secret feelings for Philip, feelings of which he seemed blithely unaware.

He had always treated her the same way from the beginning: as if to him she would always be the seventeen-year-old kid he had met all those years ago. In the beginning she had been relieved to find she could trust him to keep his hands to himself, not to proposition her or make off-colour jokes. Philip was a tough businessman, but he was kind and thoughtful to her; he treated her as if she were his daughter or his sister, and at first that had been fine. Until she had realised she was in love with him, but that Philip simply didn't see her that way.

It was from that time that her songs had begun to have a deeper tone, she thought wryly, looking back. Until then she had just been pretending to write about love; like most people when they were young, she had loved sad songs, had acted out emotions she had never really felt. Falling in love with Philip had made her work far more personal, far more real, and in the past six months she had written some of the best work she had ever done, because her grief and loss when she heard that he was going to marry Diana had made the songs pour out of her, often two or three a week, a very high production rate, for her or any other songwriter.

It had helped to keep her busy. In preparation for her new disc and the forthcoming European tour she was to make, over the last six months she had been working so hard that she hadn't had time to think too much.

For eight years she had had Philip and Diana to rely on, for help, advice, comfort and companionship. Philip was her agent and manager, and to look after her when she first came to London he had found Diana Abbot, who was then a twenty-two-year-old secretary in Philip's office. Diana had gone on working for Philip, but she had also shared Annie's flat, made sure she got to the studio on time, accompanied her on tours, and dealt with the Press and any other problems Annie ran into. A tough, capable, streetwise girl from the back streets of Liverpool, Di had a kind heart, warm brown eyes that smiled all the time and an infectious laugh.

Annie was as fond of Di as she was in love with Philip. He wasn't handsome, but he had sex appeal. Tall and rangy, with steady, cynical blue eyes and hair the colour of toffee, he was always noticed by women. Annie had had to watch him dating other girls for years, a little comforted because none of his affairs lasted long. His life was too busy, too involved with work. The girls got bored with waiting for him to ring them, and moved on. Annie kept hoping Philip would finally realise that she was no longer a girl of seventeen, but a grown woman, but she had never once imagined that when Philip did fall in love it would be with Diana.

Three months ago a mix-up over luggage had meant that the two of them had missed a connecting flight during Annie's coast-to-coast tour of America. A blizzard had raged for two days, making it impossible for them to fly on to catch up with Annie and the band. It had been the first time Philip and Diana had ever spent a long time alone together.

'I really got to know him,' Diana had said later, telling a pale, stunned Annie that she and Philip were getting married. 'Funny, I'd known him for years without ever getting past the surface, but once we started talking it was like peeling an onion; there were layers I'd never suspected. We couldn't go out of the airport hotel: the wind was like a knife, and the snow was six feet deep in places. There was a power cut, and we had no TV, no heat and no light, so we huddled under quilts, in our overcoats, and talked and talked.'

'And fell in love?' Annie had said, pretending to laugh, and Diana had turned a face glowing with happiness to her, nodding.

'And fell in love. Crazy, isn't it, after knowing each other for years? It was as if there had been a wall between us, and suddenly it fell down.'

Annie had felt sick at first. She had been hurt and jealous, bitterly shaken by this blow, but because she loved them both she had managed to hide her real reaction.

Neither of them had an inkling what the news had done to her. That was one good thing. She had never confided her love for Philip to Diana, and she had never let Philip himself glimpse it, either. At least they didn't know how she felt, so all she had to do was go on acting, pretending to be delighted for them.

And in a funny sort of way, she was—she did love them both, and she wanted them to be happy, even if it meant that she was going to be left alone, after years of being the most important thing in both their lives.

She had first met Philip at a friend's party where she had sung a couple of songs. It had never occurred to her to think of a life as a professional singer. When Philip told her he could make her a star she hadn't believed him. She had no self-confidence and very little vanity, yet some instinct had made her trust him, and that instinct had been a sound one.

Everything he had promised her had come true, slowly at first, but over the last few years with dizzying speed. First she had worked in clubs, at night, while in the daytime she had had vocal training, stage training, dance lessons, and then Phil had got her that first recording contract, which really started her career. Now she was becoming known in America, and in two weeks' time she would open her tour of Europe with a big concert in Paris.

She was becoming a star in the UK too, which brought its own problems, including getting crank calls, but she didn't often get them now because her phone was no longer listed anywhere; only a handful of people knew her number. She had gone ex-directory several years ago when she started getting problems with fans ringing her day and night. At the same time she had moved to this flat in a rather exclusive district close to one of London's big parks. The street was lined with trees; there was no passing-through traffic, just the cars of wealthy residents, or visiting tradesmen. There were big houses set in large gardens, so that one got a sense of living almost in the country, there was so much greenery around and on warm days a delicious country smell of leaves and flowers.

Even more important than all this, the large block of luxury flats into which Annie moved had a very thorough security system. There was a uniformed guard, with a savage-looking dog, on patrol all night around the grounds, and the electronically controlled doors of the building only admitted you if you had a card which you fitted into the computer by the door. You had to tap in your personal security number. Only then did the door open for you.

This was one of those anonymous blocks of flats where everyone behaved in a civilised fashion, not playing TVs or radios at top blast, not having riotous parties, not having violent rows with each other. There had been two bedrooms, one for her, one for Diana, who had shared the flat with her.

Now Annie would be living there alone, and she was finding it hard to adjust to that. She had never lived alone before. Before she met Philip she had lived with her mother and stepfather and her two stepbrothers in London. The family had all been relieved when she moved out: the house had been overcrowded, and Annie had never got on with her stepfather. She had barely seen any of them since.

Living alone was faintly nerve-racking. She listened to the silence: the only sound was the low hum of the central heating system, of the fridge in the kitchen. There were people living all around her, yet they were so quiet that it was like living alone, on the moon.

Every flat was occupied, in fact. This was a very popular apartment block; there was a waiting list of tenants wanting flats. A number of celebrities could be seen coming in and going out; often they had other homes and only kept their flat in this block for trips to London. It was well managed, comfortable, with a swimming-pool, saunas and a very well equipped gymnasium.

Life was easy here: lifts whisked you up and down, there was always a porter on the door, your garbage was disposed of by simply pushing it into a chute next to the lift. There was even an underground car park so that if fans did ever find out where she lived and waited outside she would be able to drive out of the building without being stopped.

Annie had felt totally safe there. Until now.

But it was stupid to let the phone call prey on her mind. After all, it hadn't been obscene, just some stupid joke by one of the band, probably.

Yet as she climbed into bed she was still thinking about the call. If it was just a joke, why did it bother her so much? It did; she couldn't deny it. The words kept ringing in her head. Remember me. Remember me? Had it been a question, or a demand?

Whichever it had been the intonation had somehow been disturbing, no doubt because she was here alone, for the first time in her life, feeling abandoned, left behind.

Tonight she was an easy target for whoever had rung. But nobody could have known that. She had tried to fool everyone at the wedding, tried to be the life and soul of the party afterwards—at all costs, Philip and Diana mustn't guess at her real mood. They had every right to take happiness when they found it; she didn't want to ruin their big day.

She wasn't a teenager any more; she was twenty-five, for heaven's sake! She could look after herself; she had flown the Atlantic several times, could speak French and Italian quite well, was learning Spanish—these days, as Philip said, music was an international business and meant a lot of travelling. The more languages you knew, the better.

So stop feeling sorry for yourself! she thought crossly. You've got plenty of life skills; you can manage on your own.

She could drive a car, cook; she had even had self-defence training and could throw a man over her shoulder if the need arose. Surely to heaven she could learn to live alone, and she could cope with grief and loss. You could cope with anything if you had to.

She turned over and settled to sleep, and some time during the night she vaguely heard the phone begin to ring, then cut out as the machine took over, but she was beyond caring by then.

In the morning she was in a rush to get to work, so she didn't even bother to listen to the answering machine; she simply left it switched on.

The photo session was boring. She always felt like a dummy being arranged in a shop window, and her face ached from smiling by the time it was over.

'Try to look happy, love!' urged the photographer gloomily.

'Sorry, I hate having my photo taken!' she said.

'It shows,' the photographer told her. 'Relax. Look, just a few more and we're finished.'

The band lined up behind him and made elephant's ears with their hands, and she laughed naturally.

'That's better!' the photographer said.

The drummer, a huge boy of twenty called Brick because he was built like a brick wall, grinned at her as they all walked away. 'I read in a book once that primitive tribesmen think that when you take their picture you're stealing their souls—is that what you think, Annie?'

He was the band's leading joker; the others all chuckled.

'I just hate pictures of myself!' she muttered, wondering if it had been Brick who had rung her last night, and he looked down at her slanting vivid green eyes, her sleek black hair and the small, pale-skinned triangular face which some journalist had not long ago described as giving her the look of a kitten caught out in the rain. That had made the band laugh their heads off! But it had infuriated Annie.

'You can't be serious!' Brick said, shaking his head at her. 'You're amazingly photogenic, love! And you should be used to cameras by now; your face is always in some magazine or other these days.'

She shrugged without answering. Her dislike of cameras was another of her instinctive reactions, a gut feeling based on nothing rational, purely primitive, no doubt. People never understood; she rarely tried to explain any more.

'Did you ring me last night, Brick?' she asked, and he looked blank.

'Ring you? No. Did you ask me to? I don't remember anything much about the wedding after the reception started.'

The others all roared with laughter. Annie smiled wryly. No, it hadn't been Brick, or, from the expressions of the rest of the band, any of them, either. She knew them well enough to be sure she would have picked up a self-conscious expression if the phone call had been a joke by one of them.

She and the band rehearsed for hours, not breaking for lunch, just having a yoghurt and an apple some time during the day. Philip got angry if she put on weight. It ruined the image he had spent years building up.

He was always telling her, 'Image is everything in this business! It isn't what you are, it's what they think you are that matters, and you have to be certain always to look the way they think you should.'

The public saw her the way Philip intended they should—a street singer, small, sad, lonely, defiant.

She wore her long black hair down, framing her pale face. Her make-up highlighted her big eyes, her wide mouth. Her stage costumes were simple and inexpensive; she wore mostly black, accenting her slenderness, her frailty. And although the songs changed with the years, the mood of her singing remained the same. Her fans liked her that way.

Sometimes, though, Annie felt trapped inside a persona Philip had created but which she wasn't sure fitted her any longer, even if it had when she first began singing.

'Missing Phil and Di?' Brick asked her as they left the rehearsal rooms. 'Come and have a curry with us; we're going to that Indian place down the street.'

She shook her head. 'Too fattening. I'll eat at home; see you all.'

When she got home she automatically switched on the answering machine while she was slitting open her private mail, all of it from friends in the music business. There was a letter from Philip's office about the forthcoming tour, signed in his absence by his secretary, a telephone bill and a postcard from Budapest from a previous member of the band who had left to join another group, who were touring Hungary.

Annie read that first, smiling over the few scribbled words, and then her head lifted in shock as she heard the whispering voice on the answering machine. She had been so busy all day that she had forgotten last night's crank call, but she remembered now as he said softly, 'Remembered me yet?'

The phone clicked off again, but that wasn't the end of it. The recording whirred on again. He had rung a second time; this time he whispered, 'I remember you, Annie. I remember everything.'

Annie felt ice trickle down her spine. She stared at the machine, waiting, but there was nothing else on it; it clicked off.

Who on earth was it? Not Brick. It wasn't one of his silly jokes. These phone calls were no joke. They were too disturbing to be funny. Were they veiled threats? Some sort of come-on meant to intrigue her? She had no idea what was behind them, but one thing was certain. She had never heard that voice before.

She was sure she didn't know this man, that they had never met, or if they had it had been so brief, so casual, that she had simply forgotten all about it.

Why hadn't he? She shivered, frowning. It was scary to think that out there was a man who thought he knew her when he didn't. Was it some crazy fan who had started to believe his own fantasy? She had heard about things like that; it hadn't occurred to her that it might actually happen to her.

And that accent of his... It was odd in some indefinable way, perfectly good English, but there was a faint note occasionally that made her wonder if he was a foreigner.

She was very aware of being alone in the flat. It was night again, very quiet. Was she the only person awake in the whole block of flats?

Walking over to the window, she looked out into the London sky, glowing with sulphurous yellow light from the street-lamps below. Annie gazed at the tall houses opposite, some rooms lit, others dark. There were people in all those houses, people in the other flats above and below her. Yet she felt intensely alone, and she was frightened.

The phone rang and she jumped violently. Swinging round, she stared across the room. She had forgotten to put the answering machine on again.

Well, she wasn't answering him. She would let it ring and ring; he would give up in the end, believing she was out.

She went to the bathroom and ran the shower full on to drown the sound of the phone, had a lengthy shower. As she switched off the jet of water and stepped out, wrapping herself in a towelling robe, the flat was silent again and she heaved a sigh of relief, but as she walked towards the kitchen in bare feet the phone began to ring again.

She angrily shut herself in the kitchen and made some supper: a small mixed salad sprinkled with chopped nuts and fruit. The phone still rang and rang.

He wasn't reacting the way she had thought he would. Why wasn't he giving up? Surely it must be obvious that she was out?

She wasn't, of course. But he couldn't know that. Could he? Her nerves jangled. Could he? But what if he was out there, somewhere, near by, watching her?

Her heart almost stopped. If he lived near here, or was down there in the street, he could see her lights on; he would know she was in the flat.

Suddenly a new idea occurred to her. What if it wasn't the guy who had been ringing her? What if this was Philip or Diana, ringing her from their honeymoon hotel, to check that she was OK? They would be worried if she didn't answer, at this hour of the night.

She ran out of the kitchen into the sitting-room, snatched up the ringing phone.

'Hello?' she breathlessly said.

'I wondered how long it would be before you answered,' the smoky voice said, and her heart skipped a beat.

'Why are you doing this? Stop ringing me; leave me alone—who are you?' she gabbled, hardly aware what she was saying.

'Haven't you remembered yet? Never mind, you will.'

'Look, it's very late, and I'm tired; will you get off this line? And don't ring again!' Annie shakily said.

'Are you ready for bed?' he whispered, and she began to tremble, almost believing he could see her. He knew she was only wearing a robe and was naked underneath it. 'You must be tired; you've had a long day,' he said, and her eyes stretched wide, in shock. 'I won't keep you up; I just wanted to say goodnight,' he murmured softly. 'I'll be seeing you soon, Annie.'

The phone went dead again, and she slammed her own down, panic pouring through her. He was coming here. What else had that meant?

She ran to the front door of the flat to check it was locked, stood in the hallway listening to the usual silence, waiting for the sound of his footsteps, for a ring on the door.

It was minutes before she remembered the security system in the flats. He couldn't get in; the night porter downstairs on the desk would ring her, wouldn't admit anyone until she said it was OK.

Yet somehow she wasn't entirely sure. She waited, her heart in her mouth. The minutes ticked by; nothing happened. No phone rang; nobody came to the door. She shakily retreated to the living-room, sat staring at the silent phone, waiting.

It was two hours before she realised he wasn't coming; not tonight, at least. She wondered then if she should ring the police, move out, go to a hotel, but she wouldn't let this crazy person drive her from her home. When Phil and Di got back they would be horrified if they heard about it; they'd feel guilty, think that she couldn't cope alone.

No, this was some sort of war of nerves. For some reason this man was trying to frighten her, but she wasn't going to let him. What could the police do if she told them about it? Monitor her phone calls? Maybe she should have her number changed again. But then how had he got this number in the first place, and would he get the new one too?

Who was he? How did he know so much about her?

She went to bed, and managed to sleep after a while. When she woke up next morning she had a confused memory of a dream; phones had been ringing, a voice had haunted her sleep, there had been strange, terrifying flashes of light, and for some reason she had kept hearing the sea.

It must have been the traffic of London in the distance, she decided as she got ready. It sometimes sounded like the sea when you heard it at night, and the flashes of light must have been headlights from passing cars.

She and the band rehearsed hard for eight hours that day. She had no time to think about anything else, but as she drove home that evening she began to wonder what messages she was going to find on the answerphone, and her nerves leapt as she switched on the machine.

There were none. Relief made her feel almost sick, but the next day she rushed to the answerphone as soon as she got back to her flat. This time there was a short message from Philip's office. No messages from the whispering voice. Perhaps he had got tired of playing cat and mouse with her, had given up the game or turned his attention elsewhere.

She got a card from Philip and Diana a couple of days later: blue skies, palm trees, a ludicrously blue sea and on the other side a message that made her laugh, ending with a reminder that they would meet her and the band in Paris in a week. They would need time to rehearse at the venue itself, and do Press interviews before the tour began, and Annie hoped to get in some sightseeing.

Annie was beginning to get used to living alone by the time she drove to Heathrow to catch the flight to Paris. The equipment was going overland, and then by sea, in large vans, and the band had all elected to go with it. Brick, in particular, had a neurotic fear of something happening to his amazingly expensive drums if they got out of his sight. Annie preferred to fly, though; it was quicker and more comfortable.

There had been no more of the weird phone calls; she was sleeping normally again and looking forward to seeing Di and Phil very soon. She was going to have to get used to the fact that they belonged to each other now, more than they did to her, of course. It would be painful, difficult at times; but Annie was determined to get over this first awkward phase of the new relationship. The other two meant too much to her for her to want to lose them. She would simply have to live with her feelings, as she had for years now, and maybe one day she would meet someone else, and get over Phil at last.

She would be the first to arrive in Paris, since the band would take quite a while to drive across France with all their equipment. They planned to stop *en route* at a hotel for the night, and they would join Annie at the hotel the following day.

Philip's secretary had arranged for Annie to be met at the airport by a chauffeur-driven car, and she had an escort on the plane, a couple of security men hired by Phil to make sure she had no problems on the flight. They all sat in first-class, the men on the aisle side, in case someone tried to talk to Annie, who sat by the window.

She was casually dressed in a black and scarlet skiing jacket under which she wore a white silk jersey shirt, and black ski-pants and boots. A few passengers walked past, staring, but she kept her face averted, staring out of the window, and when they landed she was whisked through the VIP channel at Charles de Gaulle and escorted almost immediately out of a side-door. A large black limousine was waiting. The two security men had words with the chauffeur in a dark suit, who got out as they approached. He held the door open for Annie, half bowing, murmured a greeting in French, and Annie climbed into the back and settled down in the luxurious, leather-upholstered interior, while her Gucci luggage was loaded on to the car.

The two security men weren't coming with her in the car; they were returning to England. A French security team would take over whenever required. The driver closed the door and got behind the wheel, then the limousine purred softly away and from behind smoked glass windows she watched the airport terminal disappear as they followed the unwinding ribbon on the auto-route.

It was some minutes later that she turned her gaze to the front again, and noticed the driver. She hadn't noticed his face when she got into the car, and now she couldn't see it, but he had smooth black hair and wide shoulders. She caught a glimpse of his neck, tanned and powerful above a white collar. He hadn't said a word to her since they set off, for which she was grateful, because now that she was in France she was nervous about practising her French. She had been learning it for years, and could talk quite easily to her teacher, but that was a very different matter from talking to French people in their own country.

She stared curiously out of the window at the boring, ugly environs of Paris, so similar to the outskirts of London and any other major city in the world, the typical urban sprawl of the late twentieth century. There was a lot of traffic, but the driver sped past it all, the effortless power of the car engine making her faintly nervous. She thought of leaning forward and asking him to slow down, but something about the powerful shoulders, the set of that dark head, made her decide against the idea.

She watched the city thicken around them on either side of the wide motorway: roofs, tower blocks, spires of churches. They passed familiar names on road signs: Neuilly, Clichy, St Denis, entry points for the inner city, but the car purred on past, and after a while it began to dawn on Annie that the driver seemed to be heading away from the city, out again into the suburbs on the other side of Paris.

Had he lost his way? Or been given the wrong destination? Or was he taking some route she didn't know about?

She was about to lean forward to ask him when they approached a toll barrier which stretched right across the motorway. The limousine slowed and joined a queue, and Annie looked up at the huge signs giving directions for the road ahead. Lyon? That was a city right in the centre of France—why were they taking a road that led there?

They reached an automatic ticket machine and the driver leaned out and took a ticket; the barrier rose and the car shot forward with a deep-throated purr.

Annie leaned forward and banged on the glass partition. 'Where are you going?' she asked in English, then in French, '*Monsieur—où allez-vous*?'

He still didn't turn round, but he did glance briefly into his mirror and she saw his eyes, dark, brilliant, with thick black lashes flicking down to hide them a second later.

'You're supposed to be taking me into Paris,' she said in her badly accented, agitated French. 'Don't you know the way? You'll have to turn back. Do you understand, *monsieur*?'

He nodded his head, without answering, but the car drove onwards along the Peage, so fast that Annie had to cling to the leather strap beside her, her body swaying with the speed at which they moved. He must be doing a hundred miles an hour, she thought dazedly, watching another road sign flash past. Versailles. Wasn't that about fifteen miles outside Paris? Where were they going? Then the black limousine began to slow down again, took a right-hand turn off the motorway, and joined a queue passing through another toll barrier.

Annie breathed a little more easily. 'Are you going back on the other side of the motorway?' It hadn't taken very long to drive this far past Paris; no doubt it wouldn't take long for him to drive back into the city, and she didn't like to tell him what she thought of a limousine driver who didn't even know the way from the airport to Paris. Or was this roundabout route a trick he often played on unsuspecting foreigners? Was he paid by mileage? Well, when Phil paid the bills he could deal with this man; she would make sure Phil heard about what had happened.

They reached the head of the queue, he leaned out and threw coins into the automatic machine, and the barrier lifted. The black limousine shot forward with a purr of power, like a panther going for the kill.

Annie leaned back in the corner, rather nervously looking out of the window, waiting for him to take the motorway link road to return to Paris on the eastbound road.

He didn't. Instead he turned on to a local road, narrow and winding, and began speeding along between green fields and woods.

Annie tried not to panic. She sat forward again and banged on the window, more forcefully. '*Où allez-vous, monsieur? Arretez cette voiture.*' And then, getting angrier, and forgetting her French entirely, 'What do you think you're doing? Where are you going? Please stop the car; let me out!'

There was still no reply; he didn't even look round, but as they approached a roundabout he had to slow, so Annie shot to the door and wrenched the handle.

That was when she discovered that the door was locked, and that she could find no way of unlocking it. The lock must be controlled from a panel in the front of the car. Before the driver could negotiate the round-about she rushed to the other side of the car, but that door was locked, too.

She sat down suddenly on the edge of the seat. She was a prisoner. Her heart began to race; she was very pale and yet she was sweating. She looked into the driver's overhead mirror, caught the dark glance reflected there.

Huskily she asked him, 'What's this all about? Where are you taking me?'

'I told you I'd see you soon, Annie,' he said in that soft, smoky voice, and her heart nearly stopped as she recognised it.

CHAPTER TWO

FOR a moment or two Annie was so shocked that she just sat there, pale and rigid, her mind struggling to cope with her situation, then she whispered, 'Who are you?'

He didn't reply, and when she looked into the driving mirror above his head she couldn't see his eyes, only the olive-skinned curve of his profile turned away from her, the gleam of black hair above that. He had a strong, fleshless nose, powerful cheekbones. It was a tough face; Annie searched what she could see of it, trying to assess the sort of man this was, what he might plan to do to her.

'Have we met before?' she asked, but there was still no reply. She pretended to laugh, trying to hide her alarm. 'I'm sorry not to recognise you, but I meet so many people, it's hard to remember all their faces. Fans are always waiting after concerts, asking for autographs, talking to me—is that where we met? Are you a fan?'

He didn't look like a fan, though. She didn't really believe he was. Her fans were usually in their teens, or early twenties; they wore the same sort of clothes, same hairstyles, immediately recognisable as the latest street trend. Many of the girls dressed like her, actually, even to having black nails and lipstick, although that was something she had only done briefly, a year or so ago, and no longer did. She'd got bored with that.

This man was too old to be one of her fans. He had to be in his thirties and she thought his clothes were old-fashioned: that dark suit, the white shirt, the dark tie. Now that she focused on his clothes she began to realise what good quality they were: the suit looked as if it might have been tailor-made. It was certainly expensive; it hadn't come off a peg in a shop. The shirt and tie, too, looked classy, from what she had seen of them.

The clothes puzzled her. Clothes usually told you something about the person wearing them, and the message she got from what he wore was that he was respectable, conventional, yet what he was doing was neither of those things.

So he wasn't a typical kidnapper, either, although who knew what they would look like? This might, in fact, be a clever disguise meant to make him invisible, anonymous, someone police would discount as a possible suspect.

His silence was unnerving. Swallowing nervously, she tried, again, to get him to talk to her.

'Why won't you tell me who you are?'

'Later,' he said without looking in her direction, his eyes fixed steadily on the road ahead.

She broke out, 'Well, where are you taking me?'

'You'll see, when we get there.'

'Tell me now.' She tried to sound cool, calm, unflustered, unafraid, but her throat was dry and her mouth moved stiffly.

He didn't answer.

She shifted on the seat and could see his hands on the wheel: firm, capable hands, long-fingered, the skin tanned. They had a strength that worried her. Annie looked sideways out of the window at the green French countryside. Spring was only just beginning, a few new leaves appearing on the trees. The sky was blue but the sun wasn't hot. Where had he been to get that tan?

And then another thought occurred to her. She had noted a faint foreign accent right from that first phone call—was he French? Or some other nationality? Had he just arrived from another country, somewhere hot? Sicily? she wondered. Hadn't she heard that Sicilian shepherds often kidnapped people and held them to ransom? That it was a family trade? She looked at the driver's black hair and olive skin. He could be Italian. But she was going to Italy later on the tour; why hadn't he waited until she got there? Why snatch her in Paris?

'Are you kidnapping me?' she asked, and caught the dark flash of his eyes again as he looked at her in his driving mirror.

He still didn't say anything, though, which in itself was disturbing, because not to answer was a sort of admission. It meant he wasn't denying it, at the very least.

She burst out huskily, 'People will soon be looking for me, you know.'

His face stayed averted; he didn't respond.

'There are a whole group of us coming to Paris—my agent, the band, the tour manger... If I don't arrive at my hotel they'll call the police.'

He shrugged indifferently, but she kept trying to make him see sense.

'You can't just snatch someone without anybody noticing! When they check up with the airport they'll find out that a car collected me. Plenty of people saw me getting into your car, including the security men who flew from London with me. They saw you; they'll have noticed the number of your car.'

Would they have done, though? They had talked to
him, certainly, had looked at his car, but would they
have thought of looking at the number of the black
limousine? There hadn't been many other people around,
either; if anyone had been watching they would have
been looking at her, because she had been escorted out
to the car by security men and airport officials eager to
avoid any problems with the media.

She wasn't yet a big name in Europe, though. The
Press wouldn't have been over-excited by her arrival. She
was just starting to sell records there, so she wasn't likely
to be big news, but with a concert tour starting a week
later there might have been Press interest, so the airport
hadn't taken any chances.

That reminded her of something. 'There was a limousine booked,' she said slowly. 'Was that you? Are you
from the limousine firm? Because if you are, the police
will track you down at once.'

He laughed.

Annie's nerves grated. 'Why are you doing this?' she
asked him angrily, then something occurred to her and
in a sudden pang of hope she asked, 'This isn't some
elaborate joke, is it? I haven't been set up? Are you
taking me to meet Phil and Di somewhere? Is this one
of Phil's practical jokes?'

Phil was famous for practical jokes; the idea should
have occurred to her before if she hadn't been so unbalanced by recognising the voice that had made all those
phone calls.

'No, it isn't a joke, Annie,' he said, and the way he
said it made the panic start up again.

She couldn't breathe; she lay back against the up-
holstery, fighting to keep calm, fighting to breathe nat-

urally. She closed her eyes and tried to shut out everything else, to stabilise herself.

There was no point in losing control. There was nothing she could do at that moment; she was locked inside this car behind smoky glass windows which would hide her from anyone looking in from outside, so that she couldn't even attract attention by waving or screaming. She would just have to sit here and wait until they arrived at wherever he was taking her.

Her heart missed a beat. What would happen then? If only she knew what he meant to do to her. He didn't look like a dangerous lunatic, or a criminal; in fact she had to admit he was strikingly attractive, if you liked Mediterranean colouring: the olive skin and black hair and dark, gleaming eyes. She always had, but then she had French blood, through her father, who had been born in France, of French descent, although he had spent most of his life in England.

Annie had only visited France a couple of times herself. It had been the one country she wanted to visit as soon as she started travelling with the band. She had never been there while her father was alive, and she had promised herself she would one day go in search of the place where he had been born, in the Jura mountains, but there had never been time so far for such a long trip. When you were giving concerts you did the gig and moved on, unfortunately.

Her father had been dark and olive-skinned with dark eyes, like this man. He hadn't been tall, though; and he had been slightly built, not powerful. Annie's long black hair had been inherited from him, but she had been born with her mother's skin colour and green eyes. As a child she had often wished she had inherited her mother's blonde hair, too, but now she was glad she was a mix of both parents. She wished now that she were even more like her father.

She had adored her father, and his death when she was eleven had darkened her childhood, especially when her mother married again within a year. Annie had never liked her stepfather, and made no effort to hide her hostility; and Bernard Tyler had soon come to dislike her too. So had her mother.

Joyce Tyler knew her daughter condemned her for marrying again so soon after her first husband's death, and resented Annie's open contempt. She had twin sons a couple of years later, and became totally engrossed in them. She had always been a man's woman, never unkind, but largely indifferent to her daughter; now she was only interested in her sons.

When Bernard Tyler began slapping Annie around, Joyce Tyler did nothing to stop him. In fact she bluntly told Annie it served her right. 'If you were nice to him, he'd be nice to you. You only have yourself to blame.'

By then fourteen, Annie began staying out of the house as much as possible, because she was afraid of Bernard Tyler as well as disliking him. She started living for the day when she would be old enough to leave home for good. When she met Philip and he offered her a career in music she packed a case with everything she valued and left, knowing that her mother wouldn't even think about her again, and that Bernard and his two sons would be glad to see her go.

When she began to be well-known they had got in touch with her to ask her to lend them some money, offering a long, rambling story about financial hardship as an excuse, but Philip had dealt with that, as he did with all her financial affairs. They had been given tickets for a concert soon afterwards, and Annie had seen them briefly that night, but then they had vanished again, no doubt because Philip made it clear that he wasn't paying them any more large sums of money; and she had been relieved, yet that reminder of past misery had made her unhappy for days.

Her life would have been so different if her father hadn't died so young, her mother hadn't then married Bernard Tyler. Annie's happy childhood had ended at the age of eleven; until she was seventeen she had been lonely and unhappy. Even to remember those years now was to feel greyness steal over her. She frowned, pushing the memories away.

'You're very quiet,' the driver said, and she started, looking at him again, but all she could see was his profile and the dark sweep of his lashes.

'I was thinking. My friends are going to be very upset and worried when I don't arrive. They'll wonder what on earth has happened to me.'

'They'll soon find out.' His voice was cool, dismissive, and she flinched.

'What does that mean? Will you ring them?' Saying what, though? Telling them that she had been kidnapped and they would have to pay a large ransom to get her back?

She wished she could see his face properly instead of merely getting glimpses now and then. People's eyes usually told you a lot about them, but that wasn't true about this man. His eyes were like bottomless wells: deep, lustrous, impossible to plumb. And yet she was beginning to feel an odd teasing familiarity...

Had they ever met before? she wondered. Or had he cleverly managed to plant the idea that she knew him in her head subliminally, with his phone calls, and ever since he picked her up at the airport?

The limousine slowed, turned at right angles, and left the road on which they had been travelling. Annie looked out and upwards, seeing that they were driving between deep, sunk green banks from which trees and bushes sprang, over a winding, unmade road.

No! she realised; this wasn't a road—it was a driveway leading up to a house. A moment later the house itself came into view: not a large house, but detached, with trees and a garden around it, two-storeyed, with mossy pink tiles on the roof, the walls painted white and the closed shutters over every window painted black.

As the car halted outside the front door Annie tried to make out whether there were any other houses in view, and felt her heart sink as she saw that the white house stood on the edge of some sort of wood, which lay behind it, and that there were only fields in front of it. It could hardly have been more isolated. She couldn't see another house anywhere.

Nerves jumped under her skin. She bit her lip, feeling real fear growing inside her.

The driver got out and came round to open her door. Annie stayed obstinately on the seat, her chin up, defying him.

'I'm not getting out; I'm staying here until you drive me back to Paris. Take me back to Paris and I'll forget this ever happened, but if you don't...'

He reached one long arm into the car, took her by the hand, and jerked her forwards. He took her by surprise, and he was even more powerful than he looked. She

couldn't resist the tug he gave her. She almost fell off
the seat, and the next minute had been scooped up by
his other arm going round her waist, lifting her off her
feet and out of the car, kicking and struggling helplessly.

He carried her up the steps to the front door, holding
her under his arm as if she were a child, ignoring her
increasingly wild attempts to escape. While he was unlocking the door Annie wrenched her head round and
bit his hand; he gave a stifled grunt of pain, but didn't
let go of her until they were inside the house and he had
kicked the front door shut behind them.

Slowly he lowered her feet to the floor, his arm still
round her waist, holding her tightly against him so that
she helplessly slithered down his body, aware of every
slow, deliberate contact, her breasts brushing his chest,
their thighs touching, the warmth of his skin reaching
her through their clothes. The effect was electrifying.
She didn't want to feel it, but she did: a deep physical
wrench that made her almost giddy. Breathless and
shuddering, she tried to push away once she was standing
up, on her feet, but his arm was immovable; she couldn't
break the lock he had on her. Her long black hair
dishevelled, a mass of it falling over her face, she watched
him through it, her almond-green eyes like the eyes of
a scared child in the dark.

He lifted the hand she had bitten, looked at it. So did
Annie. 'I'm bleeding,' he said, sounding surprised. 'You
have sharp little teeth.'

And then he absently put out his pink tongue-tip and
licked the blood away. Annie watched him, her nerves
prickling. The little gesture had an intimacy that shocked
her, yet sent another of those quivers of response through
her body.

It was at that moment that she really began to be afraid, to believe that this was actually happening, that she had been kidnapped for motives she didn't yet understand by a man who frightened her and attracted her at one and the same time.

Her insides collapsed, but she fought not to show how scared she was, throwing back her head and looking straight at him, hoping she looked calm and confident.

'Why don't you take me back to Paris now, before this gets really serious? Kidnapping is a very serious offence, you know.'

'Very,' he agreed, straight-faced.

Flushing at what she suspected to be mockery, she snapped, 'You could end up going to prison for the rest of your life!'

'They have to catch me first,' he pointed out coolly, brushing the tangled black hair back from her face with those powerful tanned fingers. The light touch of his hand sent a trickle of icy awareness down her spine, and yet there was something like tenderness in the gentle movement of his fingers. Even that made Annie afraid—afraid of what might be coming, what he meant to do with her.

'Why don't I show you the room I've got ready for you?'

Her stomach turned over. She wondered if he could hear the acceleration of her heartbeat, see the spring of perspiration on her face.

If he picked up her nervous reaction he didn't show it. 'Then we'll have lunch,' he added, and she bristled.

'I'm not hungry! I couldn't eat; I feel sick!'

'You'll feel better with some food inside you,' he said, as if she were a child. 'It won't be anything elaborate—

I'm no cook—but I've got plenty of salad and cheese and fruit. It was freshly bought this morning in the market; you'll find it's delicious. And I've got a bottle of very good wine.'

'I don't drink wine!'

He raised straight black brows at her, looking genuinely incredulous. 'You don't drink wine? You're missing out on one of life's great pleasures. I shall have to teach you to enjoy it while you're here. It will calm your nerves down, relax you.'

That was what she was afraid of, what she must not allow to happen. She had to stay on the alert, on her guard against him, and watchful for an opportunity to escape. If she could only get out of the house she might be able to hide among the trees until it was dark and then walk until she reached a village; there must be one somewhere near here!

'If you want to calm my nerves you might start by letting go of me!' she told him, and without a word he let his arm fall.

She took several steps away, looked around the small, shadowy hall from which a staircase led upstairs.

'Does this house belong to you?'

He didn't answer, but she sensed from the expression in his eyes that it didn't.'

'Look, Mr . . . ? You still haven't told me your name. Or at least told me what to call you. I must call you something.'

He frowned oddly, hesitated, then said curtly, 'Marc.'

From the way he watched her she couldn't tell whether it was really his name but she didn't query it. 'Marc,' she repeated. 'You're French, aren't you?'

'How did you guess?'

He was kidding. Solemnly she said, 'A wild stab.' She put her head on one side, listened to the silence surrounding them. No sound of traffic from outside, just the constant murmur of the trees in the wood behind the house, yet there was something familiar to her about the noise. She couldn't track it down for a minute until she realised it reminded her of the sound she had heard in her dream the other night—a sound like the sea. This was it, not traffic, not the sea, but the rustle and whisper of hundreds of branches swaying and bending in the wind.

Why on earth had she heard that sound in her dream? There was something uncanny about it. It made her shiver. She had never been here before; why had this sound got into her dreams? Maybe he had rung her from here. Maybe the noise had been a background sound on the answering machine tape.

'Did you ring me from here?' she asked him, and he gave her a sharp look, shaking his head.

'The phone has been cut off.'

She was sorry to hear that, but maybe it had been telepathy. He must have had this sound in his head when he talked to her on the phone and she had picked up on it. Nothing uncanny about telepathy—she had several times had ideas leap into her head from Di or Phil when they were working together. If you were on the same wavelength it could easily happen.

But she wasn't on this man's wavelength! she hurriedly thought. She couldn't be.

'Why has the phone been cut off?' she asked, thinking that the house had the strange, echoing feel of a house which was always empty; it didn't feel like anybody's home.

'I didn't need it.'

'Then where did you ring me from?'

He didn't answer, eyeing her drily.

She noticed that from the hall several doors opened into rooms which were gloomy with shadow because of the closed shutters over the windows. She only got an impression of them, a fleeting glimpse of dark oak furniture and leather chairs, a wallpaper with trails of ivy and blue flowers.

'Is there anyone else here?' she asked huskily, listening.

He half smiled again. 'No, we're quite alone, Annie.'

She tensed, bit her lower lip, watching him and wishing she knew what went on inside his head. Or did she? Maybe she was better off not knowing! 'At least tell me what this is all about! Why have you brought me here? Do you want money? Are you going to ask my record company for a lot of money before you let me go?' Her mind worked feverishly. But even if Philip paid him whatever ransom he demanded, would he let her go? Alive?

She had seen his face now; he hadn't tried to hide it. Didn't kidnappers usually kill their victims so that they could never identify them? Fear made her stomach clench, sent waves of sickness through her.

'This has nothing at all to do with money!' he bit out, and she stared at him, afraid to feel relief. If he wasn't holding her for ransom, what did he mean to do with her?

'Then why have you brought me here?' She searched his face for a clue. The hard, insistent lines of it did nothing to lessen her tension. 'Are you sure you really know who I am? You aren't mixing me up with someone else, are you? Because you keep asking if I remember you, but I don't, and I'm sure we've never met before. I have a good memory; I'd remember if we had met.'

His dark eyes hypnotically stared down into hers. 'You'll remember Annie,' he said softly. 'I can wait; I've waited a long time already.'

A shiver ran down her back. If she wasn't careful, he would start convincing her! He didn't look it, but he must be crazy.

'Stop arguing, Annie,' he said. 'Come upstairs and I'll show you your room.'

She dug her heels in, resisting the hand that seized her elbow and tried to move her towards the stairs.

'You can't keep me here against my will and get away with it! I don't know what the penalty is for kidnapping in France, but you don't want to go to prison for years, do you? Look, if you just want to get to know me, I'll have lunch with you now, and then you can drive me back to Paris, and I'll see you again there. I'll get you a ticket for my concert and——'

He laughed harshly. 'You know you don't mean it; if you made a date with me it would be the police who kept it, I imagine. I'm not stupid, Annie. You're ready to promise me anything to get away. Do you think I don't know that?'

'What are you going to do to me?' She tried to hide her fear, but he would have had to be blind to miss that look in her eyes.

His brows met. 'I'm not going to hurt you, Annie; don't look like that!'

He sounded so convincing. She let out a long sigh, put her hand out to him. 'Then please let me go, Marc—please . . .'

Taking her hand, he looked down at the slight, pale fingers he held, slowly entwined his own tanned fingers with them. Annie felt her heart skip sideways in a little kick of awareness.

'Not yet,' he said. 'Just for the moment, you're my guest. You'll find the house very comfortable, and it's tranquil here, much more peaceful than you would have been in Paris. No media clamouring for interviews, no telephones, no fans waiting outside to hassle you. Why don't you stop worrying and enjoy it?'

Annie considered him soberly. If she kept her temper and was not unfriendly maybe she would be able to talk him round, get him to see sense and take her back to Paris.

She pulled her hand away; he let it go without comment. Annie began to walk upstairs, aware of him following close behind her.

'In here,' he said, throwing open a door on the landing above.

Halting on the threshold, she watched him walk across the darkened room to the windows. He opened them, flung back the shutters, and light flooded in, making her blink, dazzled, staring at him.

She felt a strange flash of surprise, a jerk of dislocation, like mental whiplash, and for that instant had the oddest feeling, and then it was gone, and she was watching him with wide, half-blind green eyes.

He stared back at her with a curious eagerness, as if he knew that something had happened to her just then, as if he could read her thoughts, or her feelings; and that bothered her. That could be very dangerous. From now on she must try to hide from him what she was thinking, or she would have no defences against him.

'Annie?' he whispered.

'Where's the bathroom?' she asked, trying to keep all intonation out of her voice.

She thought she heard him sigh. Then he gestured. 'Through that door. I'll go downstairs and start preparing lunch, so don't be long. I'll bring your cases in from the car later and you can unpack after lunch.'

She waited until she heard him reach the bottom of the stairs, then she went over to the window. How far was it to the ground from up here? If there was a handy drainpipe it might be worth risking the climb down. She peered down at the garden below and grimaced. No, that was out.

There was no drainpipe close enough—the nearest was outside the bathroom, and the bathroom window looked far too small for her to climb through it. From here, too, the ground seemed a very long way off. She wouldn't like to risk breaking a leg, or worse, by jumping out of the window. In films people knotted sheets together and climbed down them; maybe she could try that.

But not now. She could hear noises from the room below, a tap running, the sound of china clattering. That must be the kitchen. If she tried to climb out of here now he'd be sure to spot her.

She went into the bathroom and found it very pretty: the fittings a primrose-yellow, a pine shelf along the wall filled with French toiletries—bath oil, soaps, gels, shampoo, talc.

Annie washed, then deliberately left her face bare of make-up, brushed her long black hair up into a neat bun at the back of her neck, made herself look as unattractive as possible.

Looking at her reflection in the bathroom mirror, she saw the nervous awareness in her green eyes and turned away quickly. In this situation it was very dangerous to admit, even to herself, in the privacy of her own head, that she found him attractive. No, more than that, if she was honest. Ever since she first saw him she had been mesmerised; and that was scary.

He might keep telling her not to be scared, that he wouldn't hurt her, but the fact remained—he had kidnapped her, brought her here by force. Why had he done that, if not for ransom? What on earth was going on here? She was afraid to think about it.

Was he out of his head? Look at his obsession that they had met before! Yes, one of them had to be crazy, and it wasn't her. She was one hundred per cent certain she had never seen him in her life until today.

Then she remembered that fleeting dizziness when he opened the shutters, the feeling of *déjà vu*, and she frowned, bit her lip. What on earth had that been about? For a second she almost had thought she remembered . . . something . . .

Angrily she pushed the thought away. She was letting him get to her, that was all. She must not let him hypnotise her into joining him in his fantasy. That way lay madness.

Feeling calmer, she went downstairs, started looking into rooms, until she opened a door into a large, bright kitchen with golden pine fittings, white walls and red and white gingham curtains. There were bowls of hyacinths in bloom on the windowsill, and the whole room was full of their scent and the fragrance of fresh coffee.

While she hesitated at the door, Marc turned to look at her, his narrowed eyes skating over her face and hair, his brows rising sardonically.

'You look about fifteen! Is that meant to make me keep my distance?'

'I hope you will anyway,' she said primly, not meeting his eyes.

There was a long silence, and at last she had to look up. He was watching her seriously, his dark eyes level and frowning.

'I told you, you don't need to be afraid. I'm not holding you for ransom, I won't hurt you, and, I assure you, I won't leap on you suddenly. I won't force you to do anything you don't want to do.'

Red burned in her cheeks. 'You forced me to come here, and you're forcing me to stay here against my will.'

'It was the only way I could get you to myself for long enough,' he coolly told her.

'Long enough for what?'

'To get to know me,' he said. 'Now come and sit down at the table and we'll have lunch.'

Still absorbed in thinking over what he had just said, she didn't argue. She sat down automatically and looked at the food he had put out on the square pine kitchen table—a large bowl of crisp green salad tossed in dressing, black olives in a dish, some hard-boiled eggs, tomatoes, a gingham-covered wicker basket of sliced French bread, a platter of various French cheeses and a bowl of fruit.

Annie hadn't felt hungry until then, but the food looked so good that she felt a surprising pang of hunger.

'Help yourself,' he said as he sat down opposite her.

She took salad—a mixture of avocado, lettuces, cucumber, green peppers—a hard-boiled egg, a tomato, some black olives, a slice of Brie, some of the golden bread.

'I'm sorry there's nothing more exciting,' he said, and she looked up, her green eyes startled, then smiled.

'It's great food—I've always loved a picnic; that's what this is—a picnic indoors.'

'But picnic food tastes better in the open air,' he said, reaching over to pour white wine into her glass, and that was when Annie had another of those strange *déjà vu* flashes, a baffling sense of having seen him do that before.

As she drew a sharp, startled breath he looked up at her, his body stiffening, his face watchful.

'Annie?' he said again, as he had before, and she slowly lifted her own eyes to stare back at him, dazed.

He held her eyes. 'Tell me what you felt,' he softly said.

'I don't know,' she whispered. 'It was...nothing...'

'It was something,' he said, and his black eyes glittered. 'You're beginning to remember.'

CHAPTER THREE

'WHY don't you tell me when we're supposed to have met, and stop playing games?' Annie burst out.

Shaking his head, he gestured. 'Taste the wine.'

'Was it in England? In London?'

'There's no point in trying to guess. When you remember, you'll know.'

But she was beginning to read his expressions, the fleeting thoughts passing through those brilliant liquid black eyes, the way his mouth changed, softening, tightening, twisting. He might not have denied that they'd met in England, but something about his face just then told her that that wasn't where they had met. Where else could it have been? She was determined to make him tell her.

'America?'

He laughed, shook his head.

That didn't leave many other countries. Annie hadn't travelled very widely yet. So she came to the most likely answer.

'Was it here, in France?'

He didn't answer, but his eyes were as bright as black stars.

'It was, wasn't it?' she said slowly.

'So now you believe we have met,' he said, his voice deep, vibrating with a new note, passionate, excited. She felt her pulses leap, and this time it was she who didn't answer. She didn't have to; her sudden flush, the way she looked down, her dark lashes cloaking her eyes, spoke for her.

Huskily she finally said, 'I believe you think we did. But I really don't remember—I'm sorry. I've only been to France a couple of times—it must have been on one of those trips, I suppose. The last time I came here I spent two weeks in Normandy with my best friend and her sister. We stayed in a wonderful old hotel in Caborg, right on the sea. It was very hot that summer; we spent a lot of time on the beach—was that where we met?'

He shook his head, sipping wine and leaning back in his chair, his lids half down over his dark eyes, his legs stretched full-length sideways. Annie didn't mean to stare, but she couldn't help noticing that under his shirt she could almost see the ripple of lean muscled flesh every time he breathed. He had a very slim waist and hips, or was that a visual illusion because of the length of his legs? She couldn't deny that he was her type. His long, supple body was intensely sexy.

Her eyes drifted back upwards, and with a start of shock met his gaze. Annie looked away, her colour high.

'Well, where did we meet?' Her voice was husky, defying him to make anything of the way she had been looking him over. 'If I knew where we met I might remember it. Why don't you tell me?'

'Because you have to remember without any help from me,' he said coolly.

'Why?' she persisted.

He ignored the question, gesturing. 'Come on, eat some of your salad—you look as if your blood sugar is a little low. Maybe that's why you're so bad-tempered.'

'I'm bad-tempered because you've kidnapped me!' she retorted, but picked up her glass and drained the pale golden wine while he watched, his brows shooting up.

'Careful! If you aren't used to drinking wine it could go to your head if you drink it too fast.'

She reached for the bottle, which stood in a vacuum jug in the middle of the table, but Marc lifted it out before she seized it, poured her another half-glass, refilled his own, advising her,

'Eat your food before you drink any more; it's never wise to drink on an empty stomach.'

'Will you stop giving me orders?' But she began to eat all the same, and the food was delicious—the cheese, the bread, the salad with its tangy dressing tasting of lemon, vinegar and herbs and glistening with oil. All this tension seemed to have given her an appetite, or maybe it had been the wine, after all.

Later they ate fruit and then drank some of the most wonderful coffee Annie had ever tasted.

She told him so, and he grinned.

'Thank you. The secret is in the beans; you have to grind just the amount you need each time you make coffee or you lose a little of the flavour.'

'I make instant at home,' she confessed, and he grimaced.

'Instant? No comparison.'

'Probably not, but I don't always have the time or the energy to make fresh coffee. I work very hard most days. I'm dead tired when I get home and I just want to curl up and relax, watch TV, read magazines, have a long bath, anything to take my mind off what I've been doing all day. I suppose you have the same image of pop musicians that most people have—you think we just play around in recording studios, having fun, and that most of us can't actually sing, or play our instruments, but that isn't true of anyone I work with. We all know what we're doing and we work very hard—rehearsing the same tune over and over again, constantly breaking off to work on a particular phrase, and, even when we finally get around to taping it, often doing take after take before the recording people are satisfied. It's exhausting, believe me, and hell on the throat; and when you're on tour it can be even worse because then you not only have to rehearse every day, you're doing a live performance at night, and you have to travel across country, even across continents, which is another sort of drain on your energy.'

Mildly he murmured, 'I only said that freshly ground coffee tasted better than instant. It wasn't an attack on your lifestyle.'

Flushed, she laughed, relaxing again. 'No, sorry, it's just that I was interviewed by some journalist recently who had an axe to grind about women with careers who stop off and buy microwave dinners on their way home instead of cooking a real meal for their men. We had a blazing row and he wrote an article that tore me to shreds.'

He listened, his head on one side and his eyes half veiled by drooping lids. 'There isn't a man in your life, though, is there? Unless you've managed to keep him a big secret so far.'

She glanced at him and felt the intensity of his concentration on her, sensed the tension in his long, lean body. The back of her neck prickled.

This wasn't the first time someone had got totally hooked on her; fans often went through a phase of obsessive devotion, especially at first. For some of them their favourite star became an icon they could worship from afar, yearning all the time to get closer and closer. Annie had always found that sort of fan disturbing, but so far none of them had ever come this close; she had never needed to be physically afraid of what one of them might do, although now and then she had a recurring nightmare about the death of John Lennon. She knew with one part of her mind that that wasn't likely to happen to her, that she simply wasn't world-famous enough to attract that sort of craziness, but when she noticed one particular male fan hanging around outside her home, outside the studio, peering into her car as she drove out, gazing fixedly at her, she always felt ice trickle down her spine.

As she hadn't answered him, Marc repeated tensely, 'Have you got a lover?'

She meant to refuse to answer, but the darkness in his eyes drew the word out of her.

'No,' she whispered, and heard the intake of his breath, saw the satisfied flash of his eyes. Hurriedly she got up and began clearing the table. Marc helped her, showing her how to stack things in the dishwasher and put it on. When the kitchen was spotless again he said, 'I'll get your cases in from the car now, shall I?'

He had seemed so reasonable while they were working together, handing plates to each other, putting stuff away, that Annie went back to pleading with him, her green eyes, wide, coaxing, 'Please take me to Paris; don't go on with this. My friends will have started looking for me by now; they'll have called the police.'

'Nobody's expecting you until tomorrow,' he coolly informed her. 'The hotel has been told you're visiting a friend for a day or two.'

She drew breath sharply, her eyes very dark. 'Who told them that? You?'

He nodded. 'I rang your hotel from my car while you were upstairs.' He watched her face change, smiled wryly. 'And before you get too hopeful, my car has a security lock on it, and I carry the car keys on me all the time.'

'How long are you planning to keep me here?' she broke out.

'Just for tonight.'

She stiffened, her heart began thudding painfully behind her ribs. What did he have planned for her to-night? Her green eyes flickered as she stared at him, seeing him through a veil of disturbed awareness, a primitive rhythm beating in her veins as she faced what he was spelling out for her. He had kidnapped her, brought her here, and tonight he obviously meant to have her.

Annie felt her stomach clench. What chance did she have of stopping him? He was far too big, too powerful for her to fight. There would be no contest. Her only hope would be to hit him with something heavy before he knew what was coming, and the thought of physical violence made her feel faintly sick. Would she actually be able to do anything like that?

He might bleed. She might kill him. She bit her lip, shivering. Her throat husky, raw, she muttered, 'If my manager arrives and finds I'm not at the hotel he's going to start a panic, whatever story you've given the hotel. He knows I don't have friends in France.'

'Your manager is the guy on honeymoon at the moment, though, isn't he? Why should he cut his honeymoon short? You used to share your flat with Diana Abbot, the girl he married, didn't you?'

Annie was almost past getting a shock every time he revealed how much he knew about her, but hearing the cool way he said Di's name, talked about her marrying Phil, made her nerves bristle again, and made her even angrier.

'Yes,' she said curtly. 'I suppose there's no point in asking how you know all that.'

He gave her a sideways, amused look. 'I read newspapers. It was all in there—or don't you read your own Press? The wedding got quite a bit of coverage, and every newspaper mentioned the fact that the bride was your oldest friend, Diana Abbot, who had been sharing your flat for years, acting as some sort of secretary-cum-bodyguard, dealing with your fan mail and the Press and all the jobs you didn't have time to do. One or two papers speculated on what you would do now, whether you'd be living alone or whether someone else would take over her job.'

Slowly Annie said, 'You rang me for the first time that night...after the wedding...'

Nodding, he watched her, his dark eyes narrowed and intent, while she thought about that.

'You hoped I'd be alone when I got back to the flat, didn't you? You hoped that after a very emotional day, which most wedding days are for everyone concerned, I'd be wide open to your spooky little messages.' She looked at him contemptuously. 'It was a nasty, deliberate little campaign, wasn't it? It was meant to scare the life out of me while I was all alone in my flat and feeling low. What are you, some sort of sadist? Do you get your kicks from terrifying women?'

'I'd hardly call my message terrifying. It was only two words.' He held her gaze, softly said them again. 'Remember me.'

A shudder ran down her spine, just as it had the first time she heard him say it.

'What's so terrifying about that?' he asked, and of course he was right. Two simple little words could hardly be called terrifying—they weren't even a threat—and she could have listened, shrugged, walked away without thinking about the odd message again, but for some reason she couldn't explain even to herself she had been struck by the words, the tone, the voice. They had haunted her sleep, and next day there had been the other calls to reinforce the effect of the first one, and, finally, the promise that he would see her soon.

'It was mysterious, though; and I was feeling very strung-up,' she said curtly. 'Don't tell me you didn't guess the effect it would have, or mean it to have that effect, because I'm sure you did. You strike me as a man who works out every move he makes before he makes it, and doesn't miss a trick!'

'I chose my moment very carefully, it's true,' he admitted shamelessly. 'When I heard that your flatmate was getting married a short time before you started your European tour in France I saw that this would be the right time to get in touch with you.'

'Kidnap me, you mean!' she threw back at him, wondering how long he had been planning it, inwardly shuddering at the thought of what lay behind all this—his obsession, his private fantasy.

'There was no other way to do it,' he said coolly, and her over-bright green eyes watched him with apprehension, yet he still sounded rational, even reasonable, as he added, 'I had to talk to you. I knew your tour was just starting, that you'd only be in France for a short time, and then you would be off on your travels for weeks on end with very little spare time. This was a window of opportunity—just a couple of days when I could be alone with you before the rest of your entourage caught up with you.'

'Just a couple of days?' she repeated slowly, watching him. 'And then you'll let me go?' But she was still afraid to believe him.

'You'll be back in Paris tomorrow night,' he quietly insisted.

'Why should I believe anything you say?' she challenged, and he held her stare again, his eyes level, darkly brooding.

'You can believe that. I give you my word of honour. You'll be safely back in your hotel by the time your friends start looking for you. Whatever happens between us.'

The words hit her like gunfire. Whatever happened between them? Dry-mouthed in shock, she looked down, a tremor running through her, suddenly visualising what could happen, his tanned body naked, moving above her with the supple power she had been aware of from the start, his hands touching her, his mouth...

Appalled, she broke off the thought, pulling herself together. What on earth was happening to her? What was she thinking about?

But was it her mind that had been taken over, or her body? she wondered, very aware of him inches away, his black eyes watching her with that worrying intensity. If she was thinking about him making love to her it was because her body had begun to respond to him sensually. Mind and body were inextricably linked, after all; you couldn't separate them. Nerves and senses, blood and cells, were all part of the same entity; touch one and you touched them all.

This man was attempting to do more than get to know her, though; she felt sure of that. He wanted to take her over entirely, body and soul. She felt herself the focus of a desire that frightened yet excited her, even while she angrily resisted it.

'I'll get your cases and you can unpack what you need for tonight,' he coolly said, and walked out of the kitchen.

Annie followed him down the hall, but he turned at the front door and said, 'Wait upstairs. I'll bring the cases up to you.'

He didn't want her trying to escape, of course. She reluctantly began to climb the stairs and he stood, watching her, until she reached the landing and went into the bedroom he had told her she could use.

She heard him walk to the car, the grate of his heels on the path. She was tempted to make a run for it, but common sense warned her she had no chance of getting away before he caught up with her again, so instead she quietly began exploring the other rooms on the same floor of the house, starting with the main bedroom at the front, which was probably his room, she decided.

The shutters were closed and the dark blue shadows of the afternoon made the room dim, but she looked around it from the door with curiosity, only to stiffen almost at once as she saw her own face looking back at her from the opposite wall. It wasn't her reflection in a mirror. It was a huge, almost life-size coloured poster portrait given away a year ago in Britain by one of the teenage music magazines. He had stuck it up facing his bed.

But it wasn't the only picture of her in the room. As her stunned gaze slowly travelled round the walls she recognised her own face on every inch of available space—disc covers, photos from magazines, pencil drawings, newspaper articles, water-colour and oil paintings of her, black and white glossy stills signed by her, which meant he had got them from her own publicity people.

She had heard of fans who did this sort of thing, but she had never so far met any of them, and had always believed they were all teenagers, kids in that no man's land between childhood and adulthood who got obsessed with a role model, an icon. This man was no teenager. His obsession was far more disturbing. Shock made her icy, sent shivers through her. He had to be crazy!

My God, my God, I've got to get away, she thought. But how?

Then she heard him coming up the stairs, and her nerves jumped violently.

There was no time to run back into her own room. She could only stay where she was. She heard him pause in the doorway of the room he had told her to use. He would see immediately that she wasn't there. He dropped the cases; she heard the floorboards creak as he walked along the landing towards his own room.

A shudder ran through her as she sensed him behind her, picked up his scent, the fresh cold air which came with him, a smell of pine which was probably his shaving lotion.

'So you found my bedroom,' he murmured. 'Let's have the light on, then you can see it properly.'

He switched on the electric light. She blinked, dazzled.

'I've got every recording you ever made,' he said, gesturing.

She looked at the music equipment along the wall below the window: expensive looking, with huge speakers, she noted, set between shelves full of compact discs, singles, audio tapes and video tapes.

'Those aren't all mine?' She hadn't made that many! There were dozens on the shelves, and she didn't recognise them all.

'Different language versions of them, the French, Spanish, Italian, German...and the American versions, but they're mostly the same cover as the British edition.' His voice was casual, almost professional, as if he was an expert on this subject. 'I like the English versions best—obviously they are the original, and they work best—but I enjoy listening to the French ones almost as much. Why don't we put one of the French discs on now?'

'No, please don't!' she burst out.

'Don't you like your own work?' His face was quizzical, but unsurprised. She wondered bitterly if he had read that somewhere among all the other details of her life he had cut out from newspapers and magazines.

'That's what it is—work!' she said shortly. 'And when I'm doing it I enjoy it, but I'm not working at this moment, so I don't want to be reminded of it.'

'How do you like my room?' he asked softly, and she knew he was really talking about the pictures of her that lined the walls.

She didn't want to answer, but by now she knew too much about him. He would go on asking until she answered.

'Who did all the paintings?' she asked, and wasn't surprised when he said,

'Me.'

Taking a closer look at one of the small pencil drawings near by, which was obviously a sketch for the largest oils canvas, she said reluctantly, 'You're good. Is that what you do for a living? Are you an artist?'

He looked down at her sideways through dark lashes, grimacing slightly. 'I went to arts school for a year, then decided I was never going to be good enough to make it my life, so I gave up the idea, but I still enjoy doing the odd sketch or painting.'

While he was talking, her eye was caught by a silver-framed photograph standing on the low cabinet beside his bed. There were a group of people standing outside a gabled cottage which had a Swiss look to it, and behind the building green meadows against forested hillsides steep enough to be mountains.

Annie went over there and picked it up, took a closer, longer look. There were three people in the photo-graph—one of them clearly Marc himself, looking younger, maybe in his early twenties, so that the picture must have been taken some years ago. The other two were a man and a woman in middle age, dark-haired, weather-tanned, smiling. Annie looked hard at them both and decided the man resembled Marc, although the older man's hair was silvering. Were these his parents? And where had the photo been taken?

'What a lovely place,' she said. 'Where is it? Switzerland?'

His voice was low, husky. 'No. It's France. The Jura region.'

Her head swung, her green eyes startled and enormous. 'The Jura? But…how extraordinary. My father was born there.'

He inclined his head. 'I know.'

She should have known he would. Was there any part of her life he didn't know about? She looked back at the photo. 'Are the people you're with your parents? There's a strong resemblance.'

He smiled. 'Yes. I'm told I'm very like my father when he was younger.'

'What were you all doing in Jura? Having a holiday? Do you do hillwalking, or climb?' He looked as if he might, and his parents had a tough, outdoor look about them. Had he gone there on holiday because he knew she had a family connection with it? Actually, she'd never visited the Jura region, although she vividly remembered her father nostalgically talking about his childhood home among the hillsides thick with pine forests, their scent on summer days overpowering, and running between them the valleys rich with fertile green alpine meadows, full of cows and wild flowers in the spring and summer.

'I was born there.' He said it so flatly that for a second she didn't take it in; she just stared at him, her lips apart, her breathing irregular.

Then she repeated it incredulously. 'Born in the Jura?'

He nodded.

'What a coincidence,' she said slowly, wondering if it was anything of the kind. Had he become far more interested in her after he found out that her father came from the same region of France as himself? Music fans seized on such tiny details and blew them up out of all proportion, made them omens, signs and portents.

Coolly he said, 'No. It isn't a coincidence. It's part of the pattern.'

She gave him a wary look. 'Pattern?'

'Of destiny,' he said. 'Don't you believe in destiny, Annie?'

'I've never thought about it,' she hurriedly said, but she was not being strictly truthful. Of course she had thought about destiny, or fate, or whatever you called the strange way life worked out for you, often without your own volition. Her own life had been full of such inexplicable, surprising collisions. Her career had happened by accident, not design on her part. She had been cheerfully living day to day without any real plans for a future, and Phil had walked into her life and taken it over, forged a career for her, and was now building her up into an international star.

Phil's destiny had happened by chance, too. Oh, it had been Phil who found Diana to look after her; but after that, for years, he hadn't taken any real notice of Di, only for fate to intervene again, strand the two of them in the middle of snow-bound America, just long enough for them to fall in love.

Of course she believed in fate and destiny, but she didn't want to admit it to a man she was afraid might be crazy. She didn't want to encourage him to believe they might be fated for each other, although she suspected that that was exactly what he believed.

A new idea hit her. Sharply she said, 'I've never been to the Jura, you know. If that is where you think we met.'

The deep, dark eyes held hers. 'It *is* where we met, Annie.'

'I tell you I've never been there!'

'You'll remember,' was all he said, and Annie flushed angrily.

'I tell you we've never met, and I have never been to the Jura.'

CHAPTER FOUR

ANNIE said it with angry vehemence, but that was only because she was terrified that any minute she would start to believe him. He was compellingly sure of himself, and Annie kept getting flashes of uncertainty. Could she have forgotten meeting him? Had she ever been to the Jura? How could she have forgotten anything so important? But people did, didn't they? They had blackouts, lost whole days, weeks, months of their lives without ever being aware of what happened until suddenly the amnesia ended and they remembered everything. What if that was what had happened to her?

She looked back over the years since she'd left home and begun working with Phil and Diana, and couldn't think of any time, however brief, when she was not with one or the other of them. If she had vanished from sight, even for a few hours, they would surely have said something.

Oh, stop it! she told herself wildly. Of course you haven't blacked out any memory of him. You haven't had amnesia. This is all nonsense. Stop letting him get to you.

That way madness lay. She had to stay sane, rational, bring her common sense to bear on everything he said to her.

She turned and fled, along the landing, to the room he had told her to use. She had forgotten the cases he had brought up from the car and had left just inside the door of the other bedroom. Running without looking where she was going, she went straight into them, was unable to save herself, and fell heavily.

'What have you done to yourself?' Marc was there before she could get back on her feet. He knelt beside her, pushed the spilt black hair back from her face, staring at her forehead, a dark frown on his face.

Annie felt wetness trickling down her cheek and thought for a second that it was tears. She tried to wipe them away, looked at her hand, and was startled to see blood on her fingertips.

'How on earth did you manage to cut your head?' Marc demanded, helping her to her feet with one arm around her.

'I don't know,' she said crossly, childishly sorry for herself all of a sudden.

He looked down at her suitcases, whistled impatiently. 'Look at that! Somehow or other the metal strip along the edge of the top case has become detached; it looks like a serrated knife! You must have cut your head on that when you fell. I'll see if I can knock it back in place later. Next time you might not get off so lightly.'

Steering her across the room, Marc pushed her into a sitting position on the side of the bed.

'Stay there while I get some water to sponge your head with,' he said, walking away, and although she resented being ordered around like that Annie couldn't have disobeyed him if she tried. Her head was swimming, she felt giddy, and closed her eyes entirely.

The bruise had begun throbbing; she tentatively explored it with her fingers, wincing. It felt enormous, pushing out from under her skin like a small boulder, hot and hard to the touch.

'Don't touch it!' Marc told her, returning with a bowl of water, a natural sponge, a towel. He knelt down beside her, gently sponged the blood from her head before looking more closely.

'Hmm. Yes, it isn't serious—the cut is tiny, and the bleeding is stopping already—but you're going to have a nasty bruise there. You'll have to hide it with your hair once the cut has healed up.' He dabbed her head dry with the towel. 'I could put a dressing on it for tonight.'

She still felt dizzy, but the sensation had changed. The odd whirling of her senses now had more to do with Marc being so close, on his knees beside her, his body half leaning on her lap while he attended to her head. She had never been so conscious of anyone in her life. He was having a devastating physical effect on her. She was appalled to feel her breasts swelling, round and full, the nipples hardening on them as he invaded her body space even more, his face inches from her, his body moving against her knees.

'Shall I put a dressing on?' he asked again.

She had difficulty speaking, her voice was breathless, husky, but she tried to sound calm, sensible; she fought to hide what his nearness was doing to her.

'I'd rather let it heal naturally. If you put a dressing on it the air can't get to it.'

He nodded. 'You're probably right.' He gently pushed her silky black hair back from her temples to leave her forehead bare for the time being, and Annie kept her eyes down, fighting to steady her breathing.

'How's that?' he asked. 'Any other injuries, while I'm playing doctor?' He laughed as he asked, and she forced a faint smile, shaking her head.

'No, that's it.'

'Good.'

He dried his hands, his eyes lowered, his thick, dark lashes brushing his olive skin, making it safe for her to watch him and be sure he wouldn't catch her. The gentleness and concern he had showed her just now was puzzling, a contradiction. This man who had brought her here against her will, and kept talking like a crazy man, had such a tough male face and body, but could yet be as gentle as a woman when he chose, showing a tenderness, a caring, that surprised her.

He looked up at that moment, too quickly for her to look away. She heard him draw an audible, fierce breath, and saw darkness invade his eyes. Yet they were brilliant, lustrous, glowing. She couldn't look away from them; she felt as if she had fallen into them and was drowning.

'Annie,' he whispered, and laid the palm of one hand along her cheek, caressing her.

A quiver ran through her, but she was transfixed, unable to move.

He slowly leaned forward, and she watched his mouth, scarcely breathing, waiting.

When his lips touched hers she half groaned, shutting her eyes. His mouth had a heat that spread right through her body. She liked it too much; she was afraid of how much she liked feeling his mouth against her own. She must not let him kiss her. She knew how it would end, if she did. Suddenly terrified, she pulled away.

That was when she realised Marc had had his eyes shut too, because a few seconds later he opened them, with a sound like a deep, wrenched moan, and she saw their dark irises, the deep, glowing centres like a black hole in space.

He got to his feet, pulling her up too, his hands gripping her shoulders.

'Don't,' she broke out, shuddering as she saw the look on his face. No one should feel that much. It was terrifying to be the object of such a need, so much emotion. Annie was aghast.

He didn't seem to hear her. His head came down, seeking her mouth with a blind hunger that made her heart crash helplessly against her ribs.

She twisted and turned to escape, but finally his mouth caught hers and his hands drew her closer, one of them sliding down her spine, pressing her against his body while the other began delicately exploring her from her throat to her waist, each light caress of his fingers sending waves of wild feeling through her. For the first time in her entire life Annie discovered the erotic capacity of her body. Her skin was burning; she felt as if she had a fever which made her ache from head to foot, made her bones feel as if they were melting inside her over-heated skin.

Her fingers curled into his shirt, holding on to him to stop herself falling down.

She had never been kissed like that in her life before. It wasn't even like being kissed. It was like being absorbed, taken into him. She didn't know how to respond; she just shut her eyes and held on to him, light-headed, almost delirious.

He began undoing the buttons on her white silk jersey shirt; she felt his fingers shaking as they slid inside and touched the lacy bra underneath the shirt, pushed the lace aside and found the warm, smooth flesh of her breasts.

Annie's body arched helplessly, a hoarse, wordless sound of pleasure moaning in her throat.

'Annie, Annie,' he whispered, and she felt him shudder, then he broke off the kiss and lifted his head.

Pleasure still reverberated inside her; it was hard to come back from where he had taken her, but she slowly opened her eyes and looked up at him.

'Have you ever been to bed with anyone?' he asked in a low, rough voice.

She instantly prickled with resentment. 'How many times do I have to tell you? My private life is nothing to do with you! Stop asking me questions like that!'

He went on watching her closely. 'I have read the odd hint that your manager was your boyfriend.'

A flush crept into her face. 'Newspapers are always inventing stuff like that!'

His eyes narrowed, penetrating intelligence in their darkness. 'But was it all invention?'

She couldn't hold his stare; she looked away, her chin lifted, conscious of a quick-beating pulse at her temples, in her throat. 'There was never anything between me and Phil.'

It was true, after all. Phil had never had a clue that her feelings were anything more personal than a warm affection. She was sure he had never guessed. He would have betrayed awareness if he had, because although Phil was a hard-headed businessman he was hopeless where feelings were concerned; and Annie could never remember so much as a self-conscious glance. Phil had always been blind about love; that was why it had taken him so long to realise how he really felt about Diana, how she felt about him. Those feelings must have been buried beneath the surface for years before fate took a hand and brought them together, and suddenly Annie was grateful that she had never betrayed herself by look or word. At least she had no painful memories to forget.

'How did you feel when he married your flatmate, though?' Marc persisted.

'I was their bridesmaid! I wouldn't have been if I hadn't been very happy for them!' Defiance made her eyes very green. He wasn't getting any more personal revelations out of her, if that was what he was angling for! 'What are you, a reporter?' she sarcastically asked, and as she said it the idea suddenly made sense. She looked sharply at him, wondering if she had hit the nail on the head, but he just laughed.

'No, I'm not a journalist, Annie.'

'What are you then? You must have a job.'

'I'm a businessman.'

'What business?'

He shrugged. 'Never mind that now...'

'If you can ask questions, so can I!'

'If you can evade answering, so can I!' he mocked, laughing. 'Tell me about this manager of yours...he's attractive, and from what I've heard he runs your life and has done ever since you were seventeen. Is it true that he was very possessive with you, didn't allow you to date, wouldn't let you go anywhere alone, kept you locked away when you weren't singing?'

Angrily she snapped, 'Of course not! All that was just dreamt up by media people Phil wouldn't allow to interview me! They couldn't get to me, so they invented spiteful gossip. That's the way they operate. If you don't co-operate, they get their own back another way.'

'He changed your entire life, though, didn't he? You must have been grateful; maybe a little in love with him?'

'Maybe a little, once.' She heard herself admit it with fury and amazement. How had he got that out of her? She hadn't meant to tell him anything. Hot colour rolled up her face, she bit her lip.

'It wasn't serious, though?' He sounded as if he cared, as if her answer mattered.

She had to answer; she couldn't let him think she was seriously in love with Phil. 'No, it wasn't! But I still say it's none of your business! It was never serious, anyway. I just had a thing about him for a while. Way back, before he started dating Di.'

Marc nodded, as if the answer was what he wanted, or had been expecting. 'And was there ever anyone else?'

Her temper flared again. 'Don't you ever give up?'

'No, never.' His face was intent, pale; his voice deepened, husky and not quite steady. 'Annie, I must know if I've been your only lover.'

She gasped. 'You aren't ever going to be my lover!'

'I was, and I will be, Annie,' he said in that deep, smoky voice.

For a moment she simply didn't take it in, and then she flushed to her hairline, her green eyes wild. 'What are you talking about? You haven't been my lover! I've never slept with you.'

'Sure about that?' His black brows arched and she had that same flicker of recognition, *déjà vu*, whatever you called it. She had seen him look like that before, seen the crooked charm of that smile, heard the deep, vibrating note of his voice in passion.

She swallowed, trying to drum up her anger again. 'Stop trying to confuse me, because it won't work. There's nothing wrong with my memory. Since I was seventeen every day of my life has been accounted for— I've never been anywhere without either Diana or Phil, and they would have told me if I had had any sort of blackout, or vanished, even for a few hours.'

'Annie, listen——' he began and she furiously broke in before he could finish whatever he'd been going to say.

'No, you listen to me! Whatever you're trying to pull, you can forget it. I know I never met you before, and you certainly haven't been my lover.'

She began fumbling with the buttons on her white silk shirt, forcing them back, clumsily, through their buttonholes, aware of him watching her with those intense black eyes.

'I was, and I will be,' he said again.

Annie turned on him with something like desperation. 'You said I needn't be afraid of you, but how can I trust you now? There isn't even a lock on the door of this room. After what you just tried, how do I know you won't walk in here in the middle of the night, and rape me?'

'I won't,' he said, his mouth hard. 'But you can always move some furniture in front of the door if you're really scared. You don't have to be afraid of me, though, Annie. When you go to bed tonight you'll be as safe in this room as if it were your own flat.'

She made another appeal to him, green eyes pleading. 'If you really mean that, take me back to Paris tonight. Please, I can't stay here. I have to go back.'

'Tomorrow,' he said stubbornly. 'I need a few more hours.'

'For what? Why are you keeping me here? Why won't you let me go?'

'I told you. I just want to talk to you, Annie. One day you'll understand, but I can't explain yet. I want you to remember without being prompted; I'm convinced you will. Just a few more hours, that's all I ask.'

She sagged down on to the edge of the bed. 'I'm so tired. This is a strain for me, can't you see that? I don't need it just before I begin a major tour. I should be resting, relaxing, not being put under stress like this!'

'Then lie down now, on the bed, and sleep for a couple of hours,' he suggested gently. 'Would you like to change into something else?' He looked at her suitcases. 'Shall I unpack for you while you rest?'

'No!' she said with force. 'I'm not unpacking my cases; I'll just get a few things out of the smaller one. And if you won't take me back to Paris, then get out of here and leave me alone, for God's sake. I'm exhausted, but I won't get any rest with you in the same room.'

His face hardened, his eyes obsidian, withdrawn. He turned away and walked out. Annie ran to close the door behind him and began moving furniture in front of it—two chairs, a little table piled on top of them. They might not keep him out forever, but shifting them out of the way would slow him down and give her good warning that he was coming in here.

'I'll be back in a couple of hours!' he called, making her jump.

He had been listening. He knew she had moved all that furniture behind the door.

Well, good! she thought defiantly, opening the smaller of her cases and taking out what she thought she might need. She laid a long, lace-trimmed Victorian-style white silk nightdress and matching négligé across the end of the bed, then went into the bathroom and washed. She brushed her hair down again, looked at her reflection angrily, with dismay at the flush on her face, the feverishness in the green eyes.

She looked so different. She had changed too much too fast. He had only had her here for a few hours, but she could actually see the difference in herself, and she was afraid he could, too. Her eyes held secrets; her mouth seemed fuller, the colour of it richer after his long kisses.

She looked at her face in dismay, remembering the heat, the desire, he had aroused inside her. She still felt it. I wanted him, she admitted, shuddering. For the first time in my life I wanted a man—and he knows how I felt. Why did he stop making love to me? I didn't want him to stop, and he knows that, too.

She was bewildered. He was a puzzle, not least because of the way he seemed to know so much about her. How did he? He could have picked up facts from newspaper articles, but how did he know what was in her head? She was beginning to be afraid he would always know what she was thinking, feeling.

She turned away from her reflection and what it told her, and hurried out of the bathroom. She needed to forget, to recover from the shock of everything that had happened since she arrived in France. She had only been here for a few hours; it felt like weeks. The day had been like a wild ride on a fairground switchback. She was drained, exhausted. She couldn't remember ever being this tired.

She kicked off her shoes, took off her silk shirt and ski pants, and, wearing only her fragile camisole and lace-trimmed briefs, got into bed. Dusk was gathering in the room, birds were calling sleepily in the garden. Annie began to feel warmer as the weight of the quilt reached her. She slowly fell asleep.

Afterwards she realised she must have been asleep for several hours before the dream began.

She dreamt she was wandering into the edge of a pine forest. She was alone, but she was looking out for someone, expecting someone to come. The air was full of the scent of pine and green fern, yellow-starred gorse. A slanting sunlight came down through the tall trees, twigs and pine-cones crackled underfoot, and a few birds flew past, but further in there was darkness, deep black shadow and a brooding silence.

Annie walked slowly until she reached a little clearing. Someone moved among the trees and she turned to watch, her pulses racing.

A tall, dark figure came out into the sunlight, into the clearing, and she saw his face.

Her heart lifted; she began to run, filled with joy, holding out her arms. He caught her, lifted her up into the air, and began kissing her, swung round and round with her held tightly against him, her feet off the ground, flying in a circle.

The dream dissolved, the way dreams did, without rhyme or reason, and she found herself in another dream, but still in the pine forest, this time at night.

She wasn't walking through the trees; she was climbing upwards along a hill track, carrying a string bag which was very heavy. Reaching the summit of the hill she

plunged into the forest along another track until she came
to a small wooden hut built in a little clearing.

As she saw it she felt the same joy, the same lifting
of the heart. She began to run, but when the door of
the hut opened there was no one inside; the place was
empty, dark, silent. It looked as if nobody had been there
for years; there was no sign of anyone having set foot
inside it.

Almost before she had time to take that in, she found
herself running, sobbing, through the deepest part of
the forest, among the darkest shadow, the profoundest
silence. She was filled with a sense of loss. She was calling
someone's name; she wasn't sure who she was looking
for, only that she was very afraid.

Suddenly the night was split open with noise and
blinding light. There was a sound of machine-guns,
flashes like lightning, voices shouting. Annie couldn't
see anyone, but she was overwhelmed by a grief so
powerful that it was like dying. She began screaming.
Screaming. Screaming.

A voice began to shout her name. 'Annie, Annie...'
There were heavy thuds, the sound of wood splintering,
heavy objects crashing down. Light dazzled her and she
woke up, struggled up on to her elbow, looking wildly
around the room.

Marc had forced his way into the room. The table and
chairs had been knocked over, and one chair leg had
broken. The electric light had been switched on; by it
she saw Marc running towards her.

He bent down over her, his face pale. 'Are you OK?
Annie, that noise... did you have a nightmare?'

Trembling, icy, white-faced, she whispered, 'I had a
dream... a terrible dream...'

Marc pulled the quilt up around her bare shoulders, wrapped her in it as if she were a child, sat down on the bed next to her, and held her, rocking her.

'It's over now, though. All gone. You're safe, don't worry. I'm here; I would never let anything bad happen to you, you know that. I'd die for you.'

It was such an emotional promise; he couldn't mean it. She hated hearing him say things he couldn't possibly mean. Annie's common sense would never let her believe he could mean it.

She had grown up in a world where people did not love like that, did not say such things. Nobody had ever loved Annie with such passion. She was scared of the very idea of it, afraid of the consequences of believing it, in case he was lying, or exaggerating, or just using words without meaning them.

She was trembling so badly that she had to lean on him, her face buried in his shirt, feeling the warmth of his body close to her.

'Tell me about your dream,' he said, holding her.

She needed to talk about it. It was still so vivid, so real. 'I was in a pine forest,' she said, beginning to think more clearly, putting her dream in context, recognising where it had come from. 'That must have been because you talked about the Jura, about the forests and the alpine valleys.' Her brows knit together. 'I think you were there, although I don't remember your face, just that there was a man...'

But she wasn't being strictly truthful. She knew it had been him in her dream. She couldn't remember seeing his face, but as she ran into his arms she had known who she was kissing, although she wasn't telling him that.

Marc was very still, listening intently, his hand automatically stroking her tumbled black hair.

'And then...' She swallowed, her eyes shut, remembering with horror. 'It all got mixed up. I was running, crying; and then there was machine-gun fire, headlights, men shouting...in a foreign language; it sounded like German... God knows why I dreamt that. What put that into my head? Some film I saw recently, I suppose.'

Marc didn't comment; his hand went on stroking her hair.

'Someone was running among the trees, trying to get away,' she said slowly. 'I think he was shot, I didn't see, but I was so terrified, I started screaming...'

There was a long silence, then Marc asked, 'Was that all of your dream? Was that when you woke up, screaming?'

She nodded, felt her face was wet, ran a shaky hand over it, then gently pushed Marc away, pulled a paper hanky out of a box of them beside the bed, and blew her nose.

Only then did she remember that she was only wearing a little silk camisole, with shoe-string straps, which left her arms and shoulders bare. The silk was so fine that she might as well have been naked, and Marc was looking down at her, breathing thickly.

She hurriedly pulled the quilt around her again and turned angry green eyes on him. 'I can't remember when I last had a nightmare. I don't think I've ever had one that terrifying—but it isn't so surprising, is it? I'm on edge, after what you've put me through—no wonder I'm having nightmares. Maybe now you'll take me back to Paris! I shall be too scared to go to sleep tonight, after having those dreams. They might come back.'

'They probably will,' Marc said quietly, and she did a double take, staring at him.

'How can you be so calm about it? I tell you it was terrifying... I can't go through that again tonight! You don't know what it was like!'

'I do,' he said, and Annie sat still, her green eyes wide and startled.

'What do you mean, you do?'

'I had those dreams over and over again for years, Annie. I still have them.'

Slowly, trying to understand what he meant, she said, 'You have nightmares all the time?'

'*Those* nightmares,' he said.

'Those?' She was at sea, lost. 'What are you talking about?'

'The dreams about the forest, the hut...'

Annie froze. She hadn't mentioned the hut when she told him about her own dream.

Her eyes searched his face. He was serious, his dark eyes grave as he looked back at her.

'What hut?' she whispered.

He sighed. 'You didn't dream about the hut? Among the trees? A woodman's hut, piled with timber around the sides?'

She was silent, only then remembering the logs piled up against the hut walls. She had absorbed the way the place looked without thinking about it because she had been so eager to get there, to reach the man waiting for her.

Marc watched her. 'You did dream about it, didn't you?' he pressed huskily.

'Yes,' she breathed. 'How do you know? What's going on?' She tried to think, to work out what was happening, but panic and fear made her so jittery that she couldn't think straight. 'Are you conducting some sort of experiment on me? Is this one of those paranormal things? Have you been trying to put ideas into my head, using telepathy? What are you doing to me?'

'I'm not doing anything,' he assured her, but how could she believe what he said?

'Then how else could you know what I dreamt about? You must have done something to make me have those nightmares. What was it? Did you hypnotise me? People can do that, can't they? Put a post-hypnotic suggestion into someone's head, make them do things, say things, when they wake up, without knowing why they're doing it, and tell them to forget it ever happened, afterwards— even forget that they were ever hypnotised.'

He shook his head. 'I didn't hypnotise you, Annie.'

'Then how do you know what I dreamt?'

'I told you, I've had the same dreams.'

She stared into his eyes, her brows knitting. 'I don't understand. What are you talking about? How can you have had the same dreams? Why should you have the same dreams as me, and how can you know about it, even if you do?'

'Because both of us get our dreams from the same place, Annie.'

'I know that. Dreams come from the unconscious,' she retorted. 'And my unconscious isn't the same as yours!'

'We dream about our lives, Annie. About what we did today, yesterday, last year. We go backwards and forwards in time, dream about the present and the past; we mix time up, to make sense of our lives.'

Her green eyes impatient, she snapped, 'But those
dreams I had just now weren't about my own life! I didn't
recognise the place, except that . . .' She broke off, biting
her lip and he gave her a wry little smile.

'Except that you knew you were dreaming about the
Jura?'

Crossly she said, 'Well, you had put it into my head
with your photo and your talk about the region! But
I've never been there, and don't try to tell me I'll remember it, because there's nothing to remember. It's true
my father was born there, and his family had all lived
there for generations, so he said, but he never took me
there, and although I've often thought of going there
one day I haven't got around to it yet.'

'Annie, you don't understand——' he began and she
angrily interrupted.

'I tell you I've never been there. Never in this life.'

There was an odd, echoing silence. She looked at Marc
quickly, struck by something in that silence, something
in the expression on his face.

His voice low, he murmured, 'Never in this life, no,
Annie. But you have been there and you're starting to
remember. I was sure you would, with the right stimulus.
You've started following a path I've already been along.
What you dreamt about just now really happened, you
see. It was all real—the hut, the forest paths, the darkness
and then the blazing lights, the threatening voices, the
machine-gunning. I have dreamt about that for years
now. I remember every tiny detail, with very good reason.
That's how I died.'

CHAPTER FIVE

FOR a minute Annie was dumbstruck. She couldn't believe her ears. What he had said kept echoing inside her head, making no sense at all. She stared at him, her green eyes widening and stretching until her skin hurt, and Marc stared back fixedly, not qualifying what he had said, or explaining. She took a long, harsh breath.

'You're mad! Absolutely out of your tree.'

'Annie, listen——'

'I've listened long enough,' she furiously told him. 'I'm not listening to any more of this crazy talk. You need help; you've got a serious problem. But I'm not a therapist and I haven't got any interest in letting you play out your fantasies at my expense.'

She pushed him aside and scrambled out of bed, no longer caring that she was only wearing the silk camisole and briefs. There was only one idea in her head now. She had to get away from him.

Barefoot, she raced to the door. Marc was on his feet too before she reached the other side of the room; he came after her, caught her shoulder, and swivelled her round to face him.

'This is not a fantasy, Annie! Any more than your dream was a fantasy.'

'You put that into my head somehow! I don't know how yet, but I'm sure you did.'

'Oh, come on! Nobody has ever invented a way of influencing the way other people dream.'

'I told you—you must have hypnotised me!'

'And I swear to you, I didn't!' His face was intensely serious, his dark eyes glittering. 'Annie, everybody's dream life is private, personal. So where did that dream come from? Ask yourself that.'

'I don't know and I don't care!' she angrily said, struggling to get away again. He held on tightly, leaning towards her.

'Annie, it was a memory. Of something that happened, to us.'

He was so horribly convincing. Annie was afraid she would start believing him. She reacted in pure panic, looked around for something to hit him with, and her eye fell on the larger of her two suitcases, still standing near the door. Annie seized the handle, turned, and threw the case right at Marc. It hit him in the stomach. He gave a thick grunt of pain and shock, stumbling backwards, and fell, sprawling across the carpet.

Annie didn't wait to see if he had been hurt. She ran as fast as she could, across the landing, down the stairs, two at a time. In the hall, on a chair, she saw her black and red ski jacket, which Marc had taken off when they first arrived. She snatched it up without pausing on her way to the front door, didn't even dare risk stopping to put it on.

It was pitch-dark outside and there was rain in the wind, making her shiver convulsively. She let the front door slam behind her and began to run round the house towards the wood she had noticed from her bedroom window, shouldering into her ski jacket as she ran, grateful for a little warmth. There were clouds across the moon and she couldn't even see any stars, but there was enough light from the house to make it possible to see the garden paths and the wood crowding in around the garden.

She headed for a wooden gate she had observed from the window earlier in the afternoon. She had thought then that that must be the gate into the wood. Once there she would be able to hide among the trees until Marc got tired of looking for her, gave up, and went back indoors, and then she could make her way through the wood until she found a village. There had to be one. This was not an isolated part of France. Distances were always deceptive in the country. There might be a village hidden just out of sight, in any direction; but a rise in the ground, a clump of trees, could be hiding it from her at the moment.

It wasn't as far to the gate as she had expected, but as she reached it and pushed up the metal latch she heard Marc running somewhere behind her. Fear leapt up in her like adrenalin. She put on a fresh spurt, ran faster, all out, her heart beating far too hard, her breathing beginning to come in harsh gasps.

She had to get away. Had to. He must not catch up with her. Behind her she heard him getting closer. He had longer legs; he was covering the ground faster. They were going uphill now, she sensed; it was harder to keep going. Sweat had begun to pour down her body. She couldn't see in the blackness within the trees, kept brushing against them, felt branches tearing at her long, dishevelled hair.

Cramp in one leg made her double up with a stifled groan. God, that hurt. Worse, it made it impossible for her to run another inch; she would have to stop for a minute. In agony, she stumbled sideways, off the track, behind trees, leaned on one, shuddering, while she massaged her cramped leg with one hand, her breathing painful, so loud in her own ears that she didn't hear Marc's pursuit for a moment. Only when her breathing began to slow slightly did she hear the cracking of twigs and pine cones under his feet, the pounding sound as he came closer up the winding track between the trees.

She waited for him to run past her, but to her horror he slowed too, stopped. She felt him listening to pick up the sound of her; she could hear his ragged, torn breathing.

Annie tried not to breathe either. She leaned her face on the rough bark, hoping to stifle the sound of her intake of air. She was trembling violently.

'Annie!' he called. 'Annie, you can't stay out here. It's far too cold; you'll catch a chill.' There was a long pause, then he called again, 'Annie! Don't be stupid. This is ridiculous. You could get hurt out here in the woods, in the dark. There's an old quarry somewhere in there; you could tumble into it, and get killed, and if you didn't do that, you might trip over a fallen tree and injure yourself, and lie there for days in agony.' Another silence. She heard him listening, waiting for her to betray herself, then he said furiously, 'I'll find you, if it takes all night, you know! I won't give up and go away.'

She trembled violently, believing him.

He waited again, then she heard a loud crack as he moved; but he didn't go on up the path, through the wood, although the next sound seemed further away, but level with her. He was stealthily exploring the trees on the far side of the path from her, she decided.

She risked raising her head, peering round the tree sheltering her. It was too dark to see very far, and before she actually saw Marc the darkness was split by a broad yellow beam which flashed round the wood in an arc.

Annie screamed.

In that instant her dream seemed to come true. She was in a state of mindless panic, waiting for the shouting, the machine-gun fire. She didn't even think of ducking back behind the tree, and the light which had been flashing over her came back to stay still, pinning her like a dazzled moth on the background of the wood.

Marc began running towards her. The light bounced away from her, made circles in the dark; and she snapped out of her terror, stopped screaming, began running too, wildly, without thinking where she was going, just knowing she had to get away.

He caught up with her before she got far. Above her own tortured breathing she heard his, rough and dragging, right behind her. She couldn't help looking back to see how close he was, and that was a bad mistake. As she turned her head a branch hit her across the face.

She gave a yelp of pain, thrown off balance again, and Marc leapt forward, hurling himself at her in a rugby tackle. Their bodies collided. He brought her down heavily, so winded by the impact that she couldn't move for several minutes. She lay on the damp earth, breathing thickly, face down, forcibly inhaling the scent of pine cones, leafmeal, fungus. Marc was on top of her, the weight of his body making it impossible for her to move. He was breathing as raggedly, his chest heaving.

After a minute or two he shifted, but only just enough to take her shoulders and turn her face upwards. She was too exhausted to try to escape.

He lay beside her, leaning over her, their bodies touching. When he turned the torchlight on her she blinked, shuddering and dazed, unable to see anything at all suddenly.

'You're blinding me!'

'I wanted to see your face.'

'Well, you've seen it!' she resentfully muttered. 'Now turn that damned torch off!'

He didn't turn it off, but he moved the beam slightly so that it no longer shone right into her eyes.

'Your face is filthy,' he told her. 'You look like something out of a horror film; you're covered in leaves and spider's webs, and there are twigs in your hair.' He lightly brushed his free hand across her cheek, picked a twig, some leaves, out of her hair.

A tremor ran through her. His touch was beginning to be so familiar, carrying a physical intimacy that dismayed her, as if she had always known the way it felt to have him caress her, run his fingers through her hair, as if their bodies had a shared past.

And that was what he wanted her to think, wasn't it? But how was he managing to plant these suggestions in her brain? She wouldn't have thought she was the suggestible type. She would have described herself as sensible, down to earth, not easily talked into folly.

Well, you learnt something about yourself all the time, she thought grimly.

His fingertips trickled across her mouth, and to her fury she felt her lips parting, quivering with reaction. Marc looked down at her intently and she looked back in nervous awareness, her green eyes cat-bright in the torchlight.

The torch went out; darkness swamped them.

'The battery must have run out,' she huskily said.

'No, I turned it out, to save the battery,' Marc told her, and distinctly moved closer.

'I'm cold, we'd better get back to the house,' Annie said in a hurry, her nerves prickling uneasily. The warmth of his body was much too close; her ears began to drum with aroused blood.

'You always liked lying in the forest, in the dark, with me,' Marc whispered against her ear.

'Don't start that again! I told you—I don't believe a word of it; you're wasting your time!'

'But it was summer-time then,' he said, pushing his hand into her hair, stroking the thick tumbled strands back from her face. 'Long, warm summer nights...'

He was lying on his side, his other arm across her, their bodies touching closely all the way from their shoulders to their knees.

'It isn't summer now, and it is cold,' Annie said, trying to see his face against the cloudy sky. All she could see were his eyes, glittering back at her, and behind his head the race and tumult of the spring night, the wind driving pale clouds across the moon, and behind the moon the blackness of the vault of the sky.

His eyes came closer, glowing in the dark. Annie was shaken as her mind tilted again in one of those strange flashes of *déjà vu*, a wild instability making her doubt her own sanity.

This had happened before. It had.

It had happened before, in the dark, in a wood, lying on the damp earth together, with the night sky wheeling overhead. A warm summer night, the scent of wild garlic and crushed grass...

She reached for the memory, but it was already slipping away. Maybe she had never experienced anything of the

kind. Maybe he had implanted the memory in her head
a moment ago with his talk of making love on long,
warm summer nights.

She wished she knew. Was she being subtly brainwashed? Was she so fragile of identity that she was putty
in his hands, taking any impression he wanted to make
on her?

While she angrily, almost desperately, tried to understand what was happening, Marc came down on top of
her, his mouth finding hers before she could turn her
head away, evade him. He parted her mouth, kissing her
with such hunger that she lost all sense of who she was,
what was happening. Her mind clouded; she gave way
entirely, her arms going round him, her body shuddering with pleasure as Marc's hand slid down over her,
pushing inside her ski jacket, warm on the thin silk and
lace of her camisole, the only barrier between his hands
and her flesh. She was breathing so fast that she was
almost afraid her heart would stop. She wanted to cry;
the intensity inside her was so great.

What was happening to her? She caught his head in
her hands, felt his hair sliding through her fingers,
clinging to her skin, warm and vital.

His hand was still travelling slowly, tormenting her,
down her hip to her thigh, his fingers sensually exploring upwards again, caressing her skin, along her
inner thigh, inside her tiny silk panties. As his fingertip
brushed the warm moistness between her thighs Annie
felt a shock like an earthquake hit her.

Gasping, she pulled back. 'No! Don't!' she groaned,
cold with shock, shaking as if she had a terrible fever.

Marc lifted his head. He was breathing in sharp,
hurried bursts, like someone in pain, in agony.

'Annie...'

His voice was as deep as the ocean; the desire in it spiralled inside her until she thought she would scream.

'No. I can't.' Each brittle sound was forced out of her. Her throat was as dry as ashes. She couldn't swallow.

At that instant the moon came out from behind the clouds and a pale white light filtered down through the trees, showed them each other's faces.

He was darkly flushed, his skin tight over his cheek-bones, his eyes glittering with passion, frustration in the reined tension of his mouth.

Annie was white, dark-eyed, her mouth trembling and her body shuddering in the after-shock of recognising how close she had come to letting him take her.

'Let go of me!' she shakily whispered.

For a second she thought he would refuse. She was terrified of what he might do next.

Then he shut his eyes, breathed fiercely for a moment, then got up stiffly and helped her to her feet. She was shaking too hard to be able to walk. She staggered against a tree and leaned there, very close to tears.

Marc bent and picked up the torch he had dropped, turned it on, and when she made a wordless protest flicked the beam off again. As if that had reminded him, he asked her,

'Why did you scream when I started using the torch?'

'You startled me.'

'For God's sake, Annie! Tell the truth!' he snarled, and she jumped about a foot in the air.

'If you're so sure you know the truth, why are you asking me?'

'I want you to tell me. You're still trying to pretend I'm lying, Annie, and I want you to face up to the fact that I'm not, and that you know I'm not. Now why did you scream?'

She could have refused to answer, but somehow she didn't want to. She was too bewildered by everything that had happened since he met her at Charles de Gaulle airport and brought her here. The hours since then had been a waking nightmare, shock after shock; she was almost past being surprised. She had begun to need to know what this was all about; she wanted to talk about it.

'It broke my dream,' she muttered. 'All right? When you shone that torch on me, it was as if I was dreaming again... It was all there—the trees, the darkness—and I was running, being hunted... When you turned on your torch I suddenly didn't know if I was dreaming or it was really happening. I was disorientated; I went into a panic.'

She shivered, and Marc switched on the torch again to look at her, frowning.

'Come on, we'd better get you back indoors, before you catch pneumonia.'

He put his arm around her waist, and she was too weak to push him away again. She leaned on him and let him start to guide her back down through the trees to the garden of the house.

'Are you OK?' he asked as she stumbled beside him in the light of the torch.

She gave him a sideways look, her voice prickly with resentment. 'Oh, of course, I feel just great. It's been such a lovely, peaceful day, and it's ending up with me running around a pitch-black wood, falling over brambles and gorse bushes, getting whacked around the face with branches. Why shouldn't I be OK?'

'You shouldn't have run away, Annie. I told you I'd take you back to Paris tomorrow, and I will. Believe it.'

The harsh timbre of his voice was convincing. She sighed.

'I had to get away. Marc, what you said to me was so...'

'Crazy,' he supplied. 'I know. You said.'

Her temper flared. 'Well, it was! I don't know what on earth you think you're talking about, but it's scaring the life out of me. I don't like things I don't understand. Stop coming out with such weird stuff.'

'We'll talk back at the house,' Marc tersely said, and began hurrying her along the uneven path, towards the garden gate.

The lights of the house seemed so welcoming that Annie could almost have cried at the sight of them, which was stupid, considering the urgency to get away from the place that she had felt just an hour ago. Then it had felt like a prison, a madhouse; now it looked like home. She was too drained to look closely at the wild swings of mood she was experiencing; it was just another aspect of the bewildering situation she had got herself into.

When they got back inside Marc pushed her up the stairs towards her bedroom.

'Take a hot bath,' he urged. 'I'll cook our supper. How about an omelette? I could cook an *omelette aux fines herbes*; there's a little herb garden right outside the kitchen door. Chives, chervil, tarragon, parsley... you used to make a superb *omelette aux fines herbes*.'

Shivering, she gave him a hollow-eyed stare and didn't argue, although she felt like denying it, saying she had never made a herb omelette for him, he was lying again, but what was the point? She had simply come to the end of her ability to keep denying things. For the moment she was going to let remarks like that wash over her head.

In the bedroom she collected clean underclothes, a sweater and jeans from her suitcase, and went into the bathroom, grateful for the bolt on the inside of the door. She ran a hot bath, sprinkled in bath salts, and while she waited for the bath to fill stripped with trembling hands.

Her teeth were chattering. She tested the water, quickly climbed into it, groaned as heat invaded her chilled flesh again, lay there with her eyes shut, not moving.

She tried not to think, but her mind led a life of its own. It kept reliving what had happened in the wood. She felt her stomach churning; she was pierced with a desire so sharp that it was like a burning knife.

'Oh, God, what is happening to me?' she said aloud, opening her eyes. She was burning hot now. She stared at the tiles on the walls, began frantically counting them to stop herself remembering the way she had felt in the wood. She still couldn't believe it. She must be going crazy; it must be infectious, a madness she had picked up from Marc. She hadn't even known him yesterday. How could she feel this way about him, so fast!

For years she had thought she was in love with Philip. Just a couple of weeks ago she had been suffering because he was marrying Diana; she had thought her heart was broken.

At least what had happened to her today had exploded that little myth. Her feelings for Phil had been mere affection, she saw that now. She hadn't been in love with anyone else so she had convinced herself she must be in love with the man who had rescued her from the grey misery of her home life. She owed Phil so much.

Of course it was easy for her to believe the gratitude and affection she felt meant that she was in love with him. He and Di were her dearest friends, always would be, but she wasn't and never had been in love with Phil.

She didn't know what it was she felt about Marc—but she knew it was dangerously explosive, an emotional dynamite she couldn't handle and was afraid might blow her sky-high if she made the wrong move.

'Five minutes, Annie!' Marc called from outside, and she jumped like a frog in the water, sending a wave splashing over the side of the bath.

'Are you OK?' he asked close to the door.

'Yes,' she hoarsely said. 'I won't be long.'

His voice sounded calm and gentle. People could be so deceptive. 'Omelettes spoil if they aren't eaten at once, so hurry up!'

Reluctantly she sat up in the bath, caught sight of her face in a mirror and grimaced. She looked as if she had been down a coal-mine! She hurriedly washed her face, then ducked her head under the water, rinsed her hair free of any remaining leaves, then stood up, water running down her body, wringing her hair with one hand as she got out of the bath.

She towelled herself rapidly and dressed, feeling much warmer and more relaxed as she went downstairs.

Marc looked round as she walked into the kitchen. 'Only just in time!'

As he turned back to the stove his eyes flicked over her from head to foot; she tensed, waiting for him to make some comment about the way she looked. She had tied her damp black hair with a piece of ribbon at her nape and was wearing a jade-green sweater which clung to her like a second skin, and tight, smooth jeans.

He didn't say anything, however, and she felt oddly let down.

Marc lightly flipped the golden semi-circle of the omelette on to a warmed plate and put it on the table, gesturing. 'Sit down and eat it while I cook mine.'

She pulled her chair up to the table. 'This looks wonderful, a perfect omelette. Are you a chef, or something?'

He laughed. 'No, just a Frenchman.' He poured more beaten egg into the pan, began making magical passes with a fork, sprinkling chopped herbs into the centre as it formed.

Annie began to eat, her stomach clamouring for food as she smelt the fragrance of the egg and herbs. The table was laid with salad, sliced French bread, fruit, again. She took some lettuce and a slice of bread, forked up more omelette.

The kitchen looked different tonight. He had lit candles, turned down the ceiling lighting; the room had a romantic glow.

Marc joined her at the table as she was halfway through her food. 'Why didn't you pour the wine?' he complained. He picked up the bottle of white wine, poured some into her glass, then filled his own.

'Did your mother teach you to cook?' asked Annie.

'Yes, I used to help her in the kitchen after school, but my father cooked too sometimes.'

'This was in the Jura? Did you live in a village?'

'A very small one, just a few houses, a very old church.' He was eating, but she felt him watching her secretly from behind his lashes. 'St Jean-des-Pins.'

Annie had almost begun to expect it. All the same, it was like being hit in the stomach. She caught a sharp breath, put down her fork.

'My father was born there.'

'Yes. I knew him.'

Her green eyes opened wide, stunned. 'You knew my father? Where did you meet him? I'm sure he never went back to the Jura after he left there.'

'I knew him when he was a small boy.'

She laughed. 'You mean, when you were a small boy!'

His head lifted and he looked levelly at her, unsmiling. 'No. I meant what I said. He was seven years old when I knew him.'

Her ears were whirring with alarm and confusion. 'What are you talking about? How can he have been! He was born in...'

'1936.'

He could have checked up on her father's date of birth easily enough; she wouldn't let the fact that he knew that throw her.

'Yes, 1936,' she said angrily. 'And his mother took him to England with her in 1945, and he never went back to the Jura, so you can't have met him there; you can't have been born until he was...' She did sums in her head, said fiercely, 'Twenty-four! He must have been at least twenty-four when you were born.'

'Eat your omelette,' was all he said, though.

Annie was no longer so hungry, but she finished her omelette and drank some wine without thinking, only realising suddenly that she hadn't meant to drink it after she had drained her glass. Marc leaned over and refilled her glass for her.

'Did your father ever tell you anything about his mother?'

'Now and then,' she warily admitted. 'But I was only eleven when he died; my memory of him is a bit fuzzy, and my grandmother was dead before I was born. She came to live in England after the war; I've never known quite why. I think she may have been involved in the Résistance during the war; anyway, when she first arrived in London she had some sort of Government job, translating. My father didn't talk about her wartime experiences often; he just let the occasional remark drop.'

Marc laughed, white teeth flashing in his tanned face. 'Typical of Pierre. He was always a quiet, stubborn, secretive boy. He took after his father, apparently. You know your grandfather, Jacques Dumont, was killed during the first days of the German invasion in 1940?'

'I know my grandmother was widowed early on in the war.' Annie had never been able to ask her mother questions about her father's family. Her mother never wanted to talk about her dead husband, and after she remarried it was impossible to mention her first marriage any more. Annie soon learnt that it drove her stepfather into a vicious rage if she did, and she was far too scared of him to risk it.

Marc was watching her as if trying to read her expression. 'Your grandfather joined the French Army as soon as war broke out, went out one day without saying anything to his wife, came back and calmly told her he was going at once to join his regiment, and was killed a few months later, without her ever seeing him again, leaving her with a small shop in the village to run, single-handed, and just one son, Pierre, your father, who was four then.'

Annie had never heard this family history; she listened intently, without doubting for an instant that what he told her was true. It all fitted what she did know about her father and grandmother's lives.

Marc sipped some wine, staring at the candle-flame flickering between them, his eyes deep and glowing.

'She wasn't like most of the other women in the village; she had had an English grandmother and had grown up speaking English as a second tongue. She went to university and took a language degree before she married her husband. That had been arranged when she was eighteen, that marriage; her parents wanted it. They were fond of Jacques Dumont; his parents were their closest friends. They were related distantly, in fact. Annie had known him all her life. She was fond of him, too.'

She started at the name Annie, flashed a look at him, but he seemed unaware of her, his face darkly dreaming in the candle-light, his head propped on one hand, his black hair tumbling over his forehead.

'She was never in love with him, though. Nor was he in love with her, she told me; they simply agreed to get married because it made everyone happy and neither of them had met anyone else. She was twenty-one; he was a few years older. They had very little money, but it was a good marriage, because they were friends, fond of each other. There were no ups and downs in their life, no passion; it was all very calm and down-to-earth.'

Annie wasn't sure she wanted a marriage like that. Marc met her eyes and smiled, as if reading her mind.

'But when he was killed she was deeply upset. She missed him badly, as she would have done a brother. She told me once that he was her best friend, and she was angry because he had died. That was why she got involved in the Résistance after the fall of France. It helped to take her mind off her grief, and it made her feel she was taking her husband's place, as well as hitting back at the enemy. There was a lot of activity in the Jura, naturally, because it was a border area, close to the Swiss and German borders.'

'It must have been very dangerous,' Annie thought aloud.

Marc laughed. 'Of course. Oh, yes. The whole area bristled with German soldiers. The Free French Government controlled the area of France southwards from just north of Vichy, but of course the Germans insisted on being in control of the border territory; they didn't intend to let anyone go back and forth through Switzerland.'

'But people did get through?'

'The local-born Résistance people knew every inch of ground, every forest track. They saved the lives of people who had to get out of France. Escaping British airmen, for instance, who had crashed in German-controlled territory and been rescued by local people, were sent on roundabout routes into Switzerland, travelling secretly by night through the mountains and forests. They passed from hand to hand throughout that area, from one safe house to another, with guides to get them where they had to go by night. The local Résistance people often risked their own lives to get them through the passes, over the border, down to the lakes.'

Fascinated, Annie asked him, 'Were your family in the Résistance?'

He looked at her, his mouth crooked, wry. 'I was one of those British airmen, Annie.'

CHAPTER SIX

ANNIE hadn't been expecting that. She got up in a lunge of agitation, pale and shaken.

'Oh, no! Don't start off again... One minute I think you're quite sane and normal, the next you come out with something so unbelievable I know you've got to be nuts! I don't want to hear any more. Come on, I'll help you clear the table and make coffee, then I'm going to bed.'

'No, Annie,' he said harshly. 'I've said I'll take you back to Paris tomorrow, and I mean to keep my word, but that means that time is running out. You've got to listen to me tonight!' He took her by the arms, looking down at her with insistent dark eyes. 'I realise how it sounds; I can't blame you for thinking I'm crazy, but I assure you, I'm not. I think if you just let me tell you the whole story you'll start to understand, even if you still don't believe it all. Will you at least let me finish my story?'

She bit her lip, frowning. She did not want to hear any more. Indeed she was beginning to be quite frightened, not so much by what he was telling her as by what was happening inside herself. Those weird flashes of *déjà vu*, the dreams she had had, the intensity of her feelings about him, the sense she had of knowing him, intimately, in a way she couldn't possibly do—she had been trying to give herself rational explanations for all that. But however hard she tried to believe those explanations there was still a secret residue of uncertainty inside her. She kept thinking, What if...?

What if it was all true? What if she had known him once, and simply didn't remember? What if it was she who was crazy, not he?

But what he had said a moment ago had wiped out everything that had led up to it. He had dropped the odd disturbing hint, made cryptic remarks, but now he had come out with something too far-out to believe. Now she knew he had to be crazy. There was simply no other explanation, was there? Annie had never believed anyone remembered their past lives; she wasn't about to start believing it now.

'I've gone to a lot of trouble to get you to listen to me,' he said in deep, husky tones. 'Please, Annie, just sit down again for a little while. I'll make coffee, then I'll tell you the whole story.'

She looked at him, ruefully accepting that however crazy his story might be she had to hear it or she would never stop wondering what he had been going to tell her.

'I must be almost as crazy as you are,' she muttered, giving in.

He laughed, his dark eyes vivid with relief. 'You're curious, admit it. You want to know the rest of the story.'

'OK, maybe I do, even if I can't promise to believe a word of it. I have to admit, you tell a good story.'

She sat down at the table and he began making coffee with the practised speed of someone who went through the process all the time. Annie watched him move around the kitchen, her eyes intent on him, her senses reacting with intensity to the way he moved, the black hair falling over his face as he bent across the stove, the ease and suppleness of his long, lean body.

Little flames of response kept igniting inside her. Her mouth was dry, her throat hot. She kept remembering what had happened in the wood, the feel of his body on top of her, the heat of desire. It was unbelievable—that she had only known him for a matter of hours, that she kept forgetting that he had kidnapped her, was holding her here against her will, that she could be swept off her feet by a man she knew so little about.

She would never have believed herself capable of such immediate and devastating passion. It had been a shock to her, to her idea of herself, and a revelation of aspects of herself that had been hidden until now.

The coffee was bubbling noisily, black liquid hitting the glass sides of the percolator. Marc put out cups, saucers, spoons, a bowl of brown crystals of sugar, a little jug of cream, a plate of fondant mints covered with dark chocolate.

He did everything with careful precision, placing the spoons exactly at the right angle, his fingers long and deft.

'You still haven't told me what sort of business you work in,' Annie casually murmured, and got a sideways glance that turned her heart over.

He had no right to be that sexy. She wished she had met him some other way, she wished he weren't so disturbing, so different from every other man she had ever met. He wasn't going to be easy to forget.

'I'll tell you later,' he promised, taking the coffee off the stove, and bringing it to the table. 'Do you want to drink this here, or shall we go and sit in the lounge?'

'How long is your story?'

'Long, I'm afraid,' he said drily.

'Maybe we should move somewhere more comfortable, then. I wouldn't want to sit at this table for much longer.'

Moving the candles on to the tray of coffee things, Marc said, 'I've got a log fire burning in the lounge, so we'll be warmer, too.'

He lifted the tray and carried it out of the kitchen. Following, Annie watched as candle-light sent huge black shadows leaping up the walls as they walked along the hall to the lounge, which, so far, she hadn't really seen, merely glimpsed, shadowed by the blue afternoon light through closed shutters over the windows.

Tonight the room was full of the golden glow of fire-light; in the hearth burned chopped pine logs, crackling with resin, wafting fragrant scent into the air. Annie sat down in a green-velvet-upholstered chair, by the fire, holding out her hands to it, while Marc put out the candles, on a low coffee-table, began pouring coffee.

'Cream?'

'No, thanks.'

'Sugar?'

'No, thanks.'

He gave her a cup of strong black coffee.

'Thank you.' She inhaled the fragrance, sighing. 'It smells delicious.'

'Have a mint,' he said, offering them.

'Thank you.' She took one and nibbled it slowly, staring into the flames. The back of the fire was filled with a firebrick stamped with a phoenix with spread wings, the grate was a pretty black ironwork basket and the hearth itself was immaculately tidy, even though sparks kept spitting out of the heart of the fire on to the wide stone hearth.

Marc sat down in another armchair, his long legs stretched out towards the fire, his coffee-cup clasped in his hands.

'How lovely to see a real fire,' Annie said dreamily, still gazing into the flames. 'In my flat I have central heating. There's something so comforting about a real fire, though, isn't there?'

'Yes, but fire can be terrifying, in a forest,' Marc said, a grim frown etching his forehead. 'We get them in hot summers, in the Jura; they can destroy acres of trees that have taken twenty years to grow. That's bad enough, but what's even worse is the feeling you get when a fire rages out of control. You're so helpless to stop it. It leaps from place to place, tongues of orange flame, floating on the wind, trailing drifts of dark smoke, consuming everything in its path. War is like that, too. Once it takes hold it rages out of control. It takes people over, makes them do terrible things they would never have done in peace time; it changes the nature of things, blackens and ruins whatever it meets. The temptation is to run away, get out of its path, but unless you're going to abandon everything you love you can't do that.'

'Have you ever fought a fire?' she asked, trying to keep the talk on a practical level for as long as possible.

'Yes. One summer when I was in my early twenties, I was staying with my family, in the Jura, when a forest fire started. Some teenagers were having a picnic on the edge of the forest. They made themselves a makeshift barbecue site, a spark ignited some dry grass, and suddenly a fire was raging out of control. The village all turned out to help the fire brigade; we had planes bombing the fire with water from the air, but the wind was sending the fire towards the village. We thought for a while we were going to lose everything. Luckily the wind dropped and we got the fire under control an hour later. But I didn't know that until much later. The burning branch of a pine fell and knocked me out.' He pushed the heavy fall of black hair back, and she saw a slight indentation in the bony structure of his forehead. 'I've had this ever since. I deliberately grow my hair over it to hide it. I was lucky not to get badly burned too.'

'It isn't very noticeable,' she comforted. 'I would never have seen it, if you hadn't shown it to me; your hair covers it entirely.' But her mind was working on what he'd said. 'Was your head injury bad?' she asked very casually. 'Did you have concussion?'

'They said I did.' He sounded as if he would dispute it, though. 'All I know is that that was the first time I remembered everything.'

Annie had guessed as much, but she drew breath sharply, her green eyes widening.

He smiled crookedly, reading her mind. 'No, Annie, you can't put it all down to concussion. I had remembered bits of my past life ever since I was a child. I would be doing something very ordinary, like watching rain falling outside, or a kettle boiling, or someone laughing, and suddenly I would have this flash of a memory, very fast, but very clear, like a snatch of a film replaying in my head.'

Annie tensed, paling.

'You know what I mean?' he prompted, watching her, as if he had always known when she had those moments of déjà vu.

She didn't answer. She didn't want to admit it had happened to her, too, since she met him.

He went on flatly, 'It was as if an ordinary event could trigger a memory of something similar which had been followed by something dramatic. Once, for instance, after I watched rain trickling down through the leaves of a tree in a garden, I suddenly remembered seeing a woman with long, dark hair tied up in a scarf, coming through the forest, in the rain, to meet me, and I was both terrified and intensely excited.'

'That could be a scene from a film you'd seen but didn't consciously remember.' Annie was still looking for common-sense explanations.

'Yes,' he agreed in a reasonable voice, 'except that I was only seven at the time, and the emotions were so intense, Annie, far too real for them to be memories of a film. They were very personal. I knew that that had happened to me. I had nightmares that night. I dreamt I was in a forest at night, trying to escape from people who were trying to kill me. I kept running, dodging between trees, but they trapped me—the dream ended when I was shot.'

She sat rigidly, staring. 'Shot?' He nodded, and she moistened her lips with her tongue-tip, shivering. 'In my dream I heard . . .' She broke off, hating to remember.

'I know,' he said in a quiet, flat voice. 'You heard machine-gun fire, and you knew someone had been killed. That was me.'

Annie jumped up, sending her coffee-cup over, hot black liquid splashing her legs, making her gasp.

'What have you done to yourself now?' Marc was up on his feet too, looking down at her jeans, scowling. 'Did you hurt yourself? Was the coffee scalding?'

She brushed the wet material, grimacing. 'No, it wasn't that hot; it will dry in front of the fire.'

She moved her chair closer to the fire, sat down with her legs spread across the hearth, and watched steam rise from her damp jeans as the heat reached them.

Turning her head, she crossly told him, 'It was your fault, anyway, for making me jump out of my skin! Stop saying things like that.'

His face was sombre, his eyes deep, dark wells of feeling and sadness. 'I can't. However crazy you may think I am, I believe it. Throughout my life I've remembered tiny fragments of a past life, and after I had concussion I found myself reliving that life all over again. You can say I was dreaming, if you like, and maybe I've been dreaming those dreams all my life, but I never remembered the whole dream when I woke up, just had fragments of it embedded in my memory, which were then triggered by some outside event, like rain, or hearing someone whistle, or hearing gunfire.'

She was very frightened. In a voice like the rustling of dry grass she whispered, 'Or maybe you had very bad concussion and you've been imagining this ever since!'

He shook his head, his hair a dark mirror to the light, reflecting glints and sparkles of flame, and Annie stiffened as she was hit by another of those brief flashes of *déjà vu*. She had seen him sit by a wood fire before, watched the flames reflected on his black hair, felt . . . Emotion overwhelmed her; she wanted to cry, and was shaken by the depth of her own feelings.

She had never imagined she would ever experience an emotion that cataclysmic. It was like dying, a sense of despair and sorrow that kept echoing inside her.

'No, Annie,' Marc said. 'I didn't imagine it. It happened; it's well documented. He was a real man. His name was Mark Grant.'

She drew startled breath at the name, but Marc went on talking.

'Everyone knew about him, the British airman who was shot in the forest, trying to escape. He's buried there, in St Jean-des-Pins, in the little cemetery on the hill in the middle of the village. There's a very plain marble cross on the grave, with his name on it and the date when he died. That was put up long afterwards by his family when they finally managed to visit his grave, and when I was a kid we had it pointed out to us on Sundays, after church. The village was proud of the grave, of him; he was part of our village history. It was considered lucky to name a son after him. There were four boys called Marc in my class at the village school.'

Annie burst out, 'Well, good heavens, no wonder you've always been obsessed with him! Was his the only British war grave in the cemetery?'

He nodded.

'And it had become the centre of a local legend? A dramatic story like that, it must have fascinated the local children, seemed far more exciting than anything that was happening to them, especially those who had been given his name! The war must have seemed very long ago, yet romantic; history, without any sting any more. Like English children playing at being Robin Hood and his Merry Men, not really understanding the misery of life at the time. History turns into fairy-stories, in a way. I bet you played at being the English airman being hunted through the forest, and shot!'

He was frowning. He didn't answer. She watched him, her green eyes troubled, sympathetic.

'Marc, don't you see? You already had that story buried in your unconscious, from a very early age, and

when you got concussion fighting the fire in the forest
you transferred the fire-fighting to another sort of war.'

His face was dark, shuttered, unreadable. She wished
she could see inside his head, find out if she was getting
through to him, or if he preferred his own fantasy to her
common-sense version.

Coaxingly she added, 'You had had a blow on the
head; you'd lost consciousness. You know how dreams
work—in your dream you were in the forest being fired
at by Germans, and you died. I bet the British airman
was shot through the head, too! Don't you see how it
all fits?'

Marc smiled wryly. 'Except for one thing. Nobody in
the village ever told us who had been looking after him,
in the little hut in the forest—nursing him, because he
was injured when he crashed and was not fit to travel
for weeks, feeding him, visiting him whenever it was safe
and there were no Germans in the area. Nobody could
tell me what happened between the Englishman and
Anna Dumont, because she never told anyone; nobody
ever knew. Oh, one or two Résistance people would have
known she was looking after him, but not that the two
of them had fallen in love. She was an intensely private
person. So when I was a boy there was nobody in the
village to tell me about Anna Dumont, or her son. The
two of them left years before I was born. Most of her
family were dead, or had moved away. All I was ever
told was that the British airman had been helped by the
Résistance, but he had been caught and shot.'

Her lower lip caught between her teeth.

The dark eyes watched her, a question in them. 'So
tell me, Annie, how did I know about the dead airman
and Anna Dumont?'

Slowly she said, 'You must have heard something, some time, and put two and two together.'

She refused to admit the alternative; it was too disturbing. She clung to her common-sense explanations, her belief in the rational and explicable.

He sighed. 'No, Annie.'

Crossly she said, 'If nobody told you that my grandmother was involved with the dead airman, maybe she wasn't. Maybe you made that up yourself. You probably knew she was in the Résistance; you knew she had moved to England before you were born—you mixed the two facts up and dreamt up the rest.'

He shook his head.

She eyed him impatiently. 'And if you were British in your past life, why did you come back as a Frenchman?'

'I don't know why; I only know I did. Maybe because I died in France? You came back as an English woman, maybe because you died in England.'

She drew a sharp breath. She had been expecting that for some time now; it had become obvious that he believed that, but all the same it was another shock.

'So I'm my grandmother reborn!' She began to laugh, close to hysteria. 'Marc, for heaven's sake, can't you see how utterly insane all this is?'

He moved suddenly, taking her by surprise. She looked down and he was kneeling at her feet; he caught her hands and held them, looked up at her fixedly.

'You're her living image, Annie. Surely you know that? You must have seen photographs of her when she was young. Years after I had concussion, I saw your face on an English record sleeve. I recognised you immediately, even though you were younger than Anna when I met her. She was thirty-two that summer. When

I first heard of you, you were only twenty-two. That was Anna's age when she married; the ten years after that were difficult for her. A lot happened to her.' He grimaced. 'A lot happened to the world during those ten years. In France, as well as Britain, there was a depression, unemployment, worry about the future, about the possibility of another war, and then the reality, when it began. Anna had suffered a good deal before I met her, and it showed in her face. She was thin and lined; her eyes and mouth told you a lot about what she had been through. But she was still lovely.'

Stupidly, Annie felt a sting of jealousy. His face, his voice, when he talked of her grandmother held such feeling; he glowed darkly with it, a man possessed. He was in love with a dead woman he had never met, and it was folly to let it hurt her, but she couldn't reason herself out of being jealous, any more than she could reason him out of these fantasies.

Marc looked at her, his eyes glittering in the firelight. 'And so are you, Annie, quite lovely.'

Quickly she said, 'So you do know I'm not the same person!'

'Any more than I am,' he murmured, his mouth unsteady. 'My life has been very different from the one Mark Grant led, just as yours has been wildly different from the life your grandmother led. But that's just surface difference, Annie, the small details of day-to-day living—where you're born, whether you're a man or woman, how your life works out. In a sense that's all to do with the envelope of flesh you're posted back in—what's within is what matters. There's an inner core of spirit which remains, eternally.'

She was struck dumb. He smiled at her.

'Now you look even more like your grandmother. She wasn't a talkative woman. She was given to long silences; she was very thoughtful. She had long black hair, like yours, which fell almost to her waist; she used to tie it up in a chignon at the back of her head. Most of the time she wore a black dress; they did in rural France in those days, if they were widows, wore black for years, even for life, some of them. She used to sing, too, did you know that? Her voice was untrained, but it was true——'

'You can't know all this!' she broke out, shaking. 'You've invented it! Even I don't know much about her, and she was my grandmother!'

'I loved her more than life itself,' he said deeply. 'And I mean that literally. I died for her.'

Annie drew a long, harsh breath.

'She was with me when the Germans arrived. If they'd found her she would have been shot too, but they'd have tortured her first to get information about the Résistance in that area. I couldn't let that happen. She didn't want to leave me, but she knew the dangers if she was caught, not to her, but for her comrades. She was very brave, but she was afraid of betraying her friends under torture. I made her go, and then I started off, making as much noise as possible, to lead the soldiers in another direction, giving her time to escape back to the village. They had dogs and searchlights; it was only a matter of time before they caught up with me. I could have surrendered, but I knew they would probably torture me too, to find out who had been helping me escape, so I kept going until they shot me.'

Annie was furious to feel tears spring into her eyes. She did not want to be moved by his story. That made it too real, and she didn't want to believe it. Oh, obviously it was completely true that an English airman had been killed in the forest near his village in France, and was buried in the village cemetery, and it was probably true that Marc had been named after him, but as to the rest...well, how could she possibly believe him?

'It all sounds very romantic,' she said offhandedly. 'But you don't really expect me to believe it, do you?'

He didn't answer, just watched her with those dark wells of eyes.

'Because it's too far-fetched! You have a very vivid imagination; you've persuaded yourself it happened, but I'm afraid you haven't convinced me.' Trying to seem calm, Annie looked at the clock on the mantelpiece above the sinking log fire. 'And it's getting late. I'm very tired. I would like to go to bed now, please.'

She got up, and Marc did too, so that on her hurried way to the door she collided with him. Her breathing almost stopped as their bodies touched. She flung a startled, wide-eyed look up at him.

'Annie, don't go,' he said hoarsely. His face was pale; a muscle jerked beside his mouth.

'I must,' she said, starting to shake. 'I must, Marc! This has been a very long day and I'm exhausted.'

'You've got to believe me,' he said in a harsh, strained whisper. 'Time is running out. Don't shut your mind to it, Annie. I'm convinced you're halfway there already. I've been watching you all day and I'm certain you're beginning to remember, but you mustn't fight it. You have to open the door and let it in——'

A wave of terror broke over her. 'I don't want to end up as crazy as you are!'

She pushed past him to get to the door. Marc came after her, caught her by the shoulders, pulled her backwards until she was lying against his body as he stood behind her.

'Let go of me, Marc!' she pleaded, but he simply ran an arm around her waist and held her firmly, to make sure she did not break away from him again.

His cheek moved softly against hers; she felt the warmth of his flesh through his clothes, his chest rising and falling right behind her shoulderblades, the muscled power of his body a wall against which she could lean, but which, she knew, she would have little chance of fighting if she ever tried.

'Don't be scared, Annie. I wouldn't let anything hurt you, I would never hurt you myself, either. How many times do I have to tell you? You're safe here, with me.'

His head turned into her throat. She felt the heat of his mouth on her skin and shuddered, with alarm, but, even more worryingly, with fierce response, as he moved closer, his body pressing into hers.

'Don't!'

Marc's mouth softly moved upward, and Annie turned her head away to stop him reaching her lips.

'Stop it! Let go of me!' she muttered, struggling.

The arm around her waist shifted. Suddenly she felt his hand slide caressingly over her breast, and gasped in shock. As her lips parted Marc whirled her round to face him, and before she could stop him he began kissing her hungrily, her face clasped between his two hands, and Annie was helpless to stop the deep, painful wrench of answering desire which tore her apart.

She closed her eyes and kissed him back, trembling violently, but her stupid mind wouldn't let her give in to her emotions. It kept pushing questions at her, insisting that she stop feeling and think. Think. Think.

It isn't really you he's kissing! It's her. His dream woman, the woman he's been obsessed with for years, the woman he believes he died for half a century ago. His hunger, his passion, was all illusory, self-deception. She was the focus for it now because she was alive and the woman he really loved was dead and beyond his reach.

Your grandmother! her mind reminded her scathingly. Marc is in love with your own grandmother.

Crazy, she thought. This is crazy. Marc's fingers caressed her neck, and fever ran through her veins. She couldn't breathe.

'Annie, Annie,' he whispered, his mouth sliding down her throat. His hand was moving up inside her sweater, caressing the warm flesh of her breast. She moaned, eyes closed, the pleasure of his touch so piercing that it had become pain.

This is madness, she thought; when I know he doesn't even realise who he's touching, it's sheer insanity! Why am I letting him do this to me?

Because you're stupid. Because he's almost brainwashed you. But if you don't stop this, you'll soon be nearly as crazy as he is! He's kissing you because you look like her, or at least look the way he believes she looked when she was young, so he's pretending you are her. It is her he's kissing, but it's you who is going to get hurt, because you're halfway to being in love with him already.

She felt a grinding shock as the admission hit her. No! she thought in horrified protest. I'm not. Not in love. Not that.

Only a week ago she had thought she was in love with Philip. No, she hadn't just thought she was; she had been convinced she was in love with Philip! On the day Marc first rang her and said, 'Remember me?' she had been depressed, she had felt abandoned, because Phil had just married Di. Looking back, she couldn't believe it was such a short time ago—time had stretched, twisted, contorted, over the last twelve hours. She found it hard to remember how she had felt before she met Marc. It was almost as if she was someone else now, with a new view of life, of herself, of everything.

'I want you, Annie, I need you,' Marc muttered, breathing thickly, and it was like being doused in ice-cold water.

Her eyes flew open. She stiffened from head to foot. If she didn't stop him now she was going to end up in bed with him tonight. He was going to talk her into it, she knew it. That was what was on his mind, what he meant by saying he needed her. Maybe he had always meant to get her into bed, in spite of all his protests. He was using seduction, not force, but it came to the same thing. Marc intended to sleep with her tonight.

Her stomach clenched in panic and fear. She had to get away, to stop him.

He had his eyes shut, his face buried in her neck. He was off guard now. She wouldn't get a better chance.

Annie broke away from him with all the force she was capable of, shoving him violently, sending him staggering away across the room. Before he could recover she was running up the stairs. She heard him coming before she reached her room, but she was able to get inside and start dragging a chest of drawers in front of the door before Marc could get there to stop her.

He was running so fast that he almost crashed into the door, making the panels shiver. 'Annie, let me in!' he grated, and she leaned on the chest of drawers, which was finally in position, her lungs heaving, her body shaking.

'Go away, Marc!'

'Why did you panic? Did I scare you? You don't have to be scared of me—I thought you realised that now. I wouldn't harm a hair on your head.' His voice deepened to a rough murmur, passionate, urgent. 'Don't you know how I feel about you, Annie?'

'I'm not my grandmother!' she bitterly spat.

There was a silence. She couldn't even hear him breathing for a few seconds.

Tears stung Annie's eyes. Wearily she whispered, 'Oh, go to bed, Marc, and leave me alone. I've had enough for one day. Whatever it is you need, look for it in those dreams of yours. You aren't getting me to stand in for her.'

She stumbled away across the room, heard him saying something quietly, and covered her ears with her hands.

'I'm not even listening!' she yelled, and fell on to her bed, face down, tears rolling down her cheeks, shuddering with sobs she stifled in the bedclothes. The last thing she wanted was for Marc to hear her and realise that she had been hurt. Hurt badly. It was far too late for her to stop herself falling in love. Somehow, some time, during the twelve hours since they first met, she had fallen in love with him, like Alice falling down the rabbit hole, plunged abruptly into darkness, tumbling helplessly, endlessly, as if to the very centre of the earth.

CHAPTER SEVEN

ANNIE slept heavily that night, but she dreamt, and kept waking from the dream, sitting up in bed, her heart crashing inside her chest, her breathing fast and shallow. Each time, she couldn't remember where she was for an instant, listening to the silence in the house, the sound of the wind in the trees outside, perspiration on her skin. Remembering at last, her hand trembling, she switched on the bedside lamp, looked at the clock, closed her eyes and groaned because it wasn't morning yet. She was so tired, though, that once her heart had slowed down and she felt calmer she lay down again, turned off the light, and almost immediately fell asleep once more, only to dream again and wake again an hour or two later.

It was a long night.

The last time she woke up it was from a rather different dream, hot, sensuous, erotic. They were in the forest, in a small clearing, lying on the grass. She was in Marc's arms; they kissed, their bodies moving urgently. She was aching with pleasure, needing to be closer, to be part of him. And then the dream stopped.

Annie woke up so suddenly that it was like falling off a cliff.

As her eyes opened the dream was still playing inside her head. She was groaning in disappointment and frustration, and at the same time trembling and dazed, feeling like a deep-sea diver who had come up too fast and was totally disorientated.

It was a moment before she registered what had woken her up, and snapped fully awake, eyes wide with shock.

Somewhere in the house someone was shouting.

Annie turned pale. What on earth was going on? She slid out of bed and ran to the door, listened tensely for a minute.

Was that Marc? The voice was so harsh, shouting, yelling. But it sounded like him.

Was he being attacked? Had someone got into the house? A burglar? Marc might get badly hurt. She couldn't stay safely behind her barricade; she had to help him.

Annie struggled for a minute with the chest of drawers, finally pushed it back and got the door open. As an afterthought she snatched up the broken chair leg which Marc had put to one side on another of the chairs. Armed with that, she ran out on to the landing.

The yelling had stopped by then, but she could still hear Marc's voice, muttering thickly, words she couldn't quite catch.

The noise came from his bedroom. She went in there and looked hurriedly around, her crude weapon ready, her heart beating fast.

There was no sign of a stranger in there, or of any fight having taken place. Marc lay face up on the bed, his arms flung wide across the covers, tossing and turning with restless energy, making sounds that froze the blood in her veins.

Annie crept up to the bed, suddenly afraid of what she might see. His eyes were shut, a bruised look about the lids, his mouth moving, quivering, moaning, but there were no signs of any injury.

She dropped her chair leg on the floor, pain knifing through her. As if she could see inside his head she knew what he was dreaming about and couldn't bear to watch. Bending over him, she urgently said, 'Marc! Marc, wake up!'

His cries cut off with a deep intake of breath. He lay very still for a beat of time, then in the grey dawn light she saw his lashes flicker, thick and black, stirring against his pale skin; the gleam of dark eyes showed, and he let out a long, shuddering sigh.

'Annie?'

She sighed, too, with relief that those terrible sounds had stopped. 'You were having a nightmare.'

His face was pale, beaded with sweat. She was horrified by the way he looked; as if he had been ill for days. Annie had a terrible urge to stroke the tumbled black hair back from his temples, cradle his head in her arms, rock him and comfort him like a child.

'Was I yelling my head off?' His mouth twisted wryly. 'Sorry; it doesn't happen often, just on nights when the dream's too real.' He looked sideways through the pale light at the clock on his bedside table. 'What time is it?'

'Just gone six.' She didn't ask what he had been dreaming about and he didn't tell her. Tonight, she was certain, they had had the same dreams. She didn't know how or why, but she didn't doubt that it was true, and the last thing she wanted to do was talk about them. Remembering them was bad enough; the terror and grief she had felt still darkened her mind, and Marc's dreams must be worse.

'Sorry to wake you up so early!' Marc gave her a wry half-smile, sat up, pushing back his tousled hair. That was when she realised he was sleeping naked. She hadn't taken on board the fact that his arms were bare until that moment. Shaken, she looked away hurriedly from the bare, tanned shoulders, the deep, muscled chest with the curly black hair growing down the centre from the midriff, disappearing beneath the sheet still covering the lower half of his body.

Deep inside her own body a drum began to beat—heavy, rhythmic, dominating.

Her mouth dry, she said in an unsteady voice, 'Why don't I make some coffee?'

She had to get away. If she didn't he might pick up on what she was feeling, and she would die if he did.

Flushed and flustered, she began to back away, but Marc moved faster than she did. His hand shot out and caught her arm, jerked her backwards so that she tumbled down on to the bed, giving a wild cry of shock.

When she tried to struggle up again, he held her shoulders down on the mattress and arched over her, looking down into her wide, feverish green eyes.

'I've been dreaming about you all night, Annie.'

'Don't tell me!'

Remembering her own dream, she felt her face burn, and her breathing came fiercely, hurting her throat.

Marc was watching her, his eyes quick and intent.

'Annie,' he said hoarsely. He was going to kiss her; she tried to push him back as he came down towards her, but when she touched his bare skin the impact sent a wave of desire crashing through her and she cried out wordlessly.

His mouth was on hers a second later and her half-formed protest died in her throat. His tongue moistly invaded her mouth, the heat and hunger of his kiss clouding her mind. She was lost, confused, no longer knowing if this was real, or a dream. They were so close, the present and the past, echoing within each other. Her eyes shut; she didn't know whether they were lying on a bed, or on the sweet, crushed grass of a forest, whether this was a cool spring dawn, or a long, hot summer night. She only knew that this man kissing her was the man she loved, had loved once, would always love; their bodies moved closer in remembered passion, intimate and sweet and familiar.

Her fingers ran up his chest, feeling the vibrating beat of his heart deep inside the hard ribcage, his breathing irregular, rising and falling rapidly. Marc's shoulders were as smooth as silk, as powerful as the body of a stallion, his muscles clenching as she touched him, his neck tense with awareness of her caress. The very thought of him dying made agony twist inside her. He was so strong and alive. She saw the dark forest, the flare of searchlights, heard the staccato rattle of machine-gun fire, and a scream of pain silently formed in her throat.

I love him, she thought, clasping his head in her hands, the thick, warm black hair prickling under her palms, her own head lifted to meet the driving demand of his mouth. If he died I'd want to die.

Was that how her grandmother had felt when the English airman was killed in the forest?

What am I saying? she thought, stricken. I believe it; that's the truth. I have started to believe every word he says—but what proof do I have? How do I know he isn't a liar, unbalanced, that every word he has told me isn't pure imagination?

'Annie,' he groaned against her mouth. He was lying on top of her now, the weight of his body deeply satisfying. Every time he shifted she shuddered at the pleasure of feeling his body move against hers and remembered her broken dream, the frustration that had raged inside her when she had to wake up just as they had been about to make love.

It was raging now, biting into her, making her ice-cold one second, on fire the next.

Marc suddenly broke off his kiss, breathing with heaving confusion, looked down at her as if he was being torn apart, his dark eyes glistening as if with tears.

'In a minute I'm not going to be able to stop, Annie, so make up your mind now... I said I wouldn't force you, and I won't, but I want you so much it's killing me. Let me make love to you.'

'I hardly know you,' she whispered. 'We only met yesterday. What do I know about you? I don't know what you do for a living, where you live, who you really are. You've said so much, yet what proof is there that anything you said was true? You could be the biggest liar unhung. You could be crazy. How do I know?'

He looked into her troubled green eyes. Quietly he said, 'I'm the only proof I have, Annie. Either you believe me, or you don't. Life isn't a court of law; there's no giving of evidence, no lawyers, no jury and no judge. We all have to rely on our own instincts about people. I am convinced I lived before. I believe I remember some of that life, in flashes, especially the last months before I was shot. I can't prove it, though, any more than I can prove that you are a reincarnation of your grandmother, or that we were lovers for a while. You have to make up your own mind whether you believe it or not.'

Annie gave a long, quivering sigh. He was right, of course. It all came down to whether she believed him or not.

No. It all came down to feelings, instincts, emotions—those vague, insubstantial things that weren't even easy to identify, let alone prove: thistledown floating on the summer air, moonshine, flickering shadows. She didn't understand them, but she knew what they told her.

She couldn't find the words. Words were too clumsy for what she wanted to say to him. Trembling, she turned her face into his neck and kissed the warm, beating pulse at the base. Her eyes closed, she blindly began to explore, slowly slid her mouth along his smooth shoulders, following every curve of bone, every hollow in the flesh, before her kiss trickled down to his deep, muscled chest, the moist flick of her tongue tasting his salty skin. This was what she had been doing in her dream; she was dying to go on from where she had left off when she awoke.

She wanted to touch him with utter intimacy, know him as she had never known another human being, as well as she knew herself; she wanted their bodies merged, one, completed at last.

She heard Marc groaning, felt the tension in his muscles as he touched her long, flowing hair, lifting it, letting it drift through his fingers, breathing in the fragrance of the soft strands, his arms across her back, enclosing without holding her.

'Annie ... my darling ...' he whispered, and then his body arched and he gave a piercing cry of pleasure and shock as her head went lower.

This was how they had made love in her dream. Dream and reality merged. She abandoned herself to sensuality, unafraid, without inhibition, and Marc's groans grew wilder, more intense.

He suddenly knelt up, looking down at her with leaping eyes. 'We don't need this!' he muttered, unbuttoning her long, silky nightdress.

She lifted herself up to let him pull it over her head. As he tossed it to the floor with one hand, he never took his eyes off Annie.

She lay on the pale sheet, her skin even paler, satin-smooth, trembling, and yet tense with desire as Marc's eyes moved down her body, from her small, rounded breasts with their hard pink nipples, down over her flat midriff and the smooth belly to the curled dark hair between her slender, white-skinned thighs.

Feverishly, Marc slid his hands underneath her, lifted her buttocks off the bed while he slid back between her legs and began to enter her.

Annie gave a cry of pain a second later, tensing.

'Did I hurt you?' Marc froze, looking down at her.

'No, go on,' she muttered, her arms round his body, pulling him down again. She was so hot that it was like being on fire. Instinct was driving her, an urge for satisfaction that wouldn't give her any peace until she found release.

Marc tried again, and Annie bit down on her lower lip to stop herself yelling out, but her body was eloquent enough to give her away, her muscles turning rigid, locking him out even while she tried to pull him closer.

Marc lay still on her for a moment, tremors running through him. 'You're a virgin, aren't you?' His voice was low, rough.

'It doesn't matter... Don't stop, please, Marc...' she half sobbed, holding him tighter.

'Darling, I'm hurting you.' His voice was distressed, uneven.

'I don't care; don't stop...'

He lifted his head and looked wryly at her. 'If it hurts you, it won't be much of a pleasure for either of us, Annie.' He rolled off her, lay down beside her on the bed, giving a long sigh.

Annie curled round to face him, her face unhappy. 'Well, I have to stop being a virgin some time; why not now?'

'Because, my love, I'm afraid I couldn't do much about it just at the moment,' he said in a dry tone, and she looked down his body and gave a little gasp of surprised laughter.

'Oh. I see what you mean. Was that because you couldn't...? Oh, Marc, I'm sorry.' Her lashes lowered, she smiled, put her hand out, murmuring, 'Couldn't we do something about that, though?'

Marc caught her fingers, took them to his mouth, laughing, his eyes dancing with amusement. 'You learn fast. I suspect you have a naughty streak. Another time, Annie, with pleasure, but not now. You're going to have to be patient about making love—it isn't going to be easy for you at first. It would be stupid to rush it; it could put you off for ever, and we don't want that, do we?'

'No, but——'

'We'll have to take it one step at a time, slowly.' His eyes glimmered at her. 'That will be fun, too, Annie, don't worry, but the technique will need lots of time, and the right mood.'

Frustration ate at her, and Marc's dark eyes flicked sideways, taking in her expression.

'Poor Annie...you want it badly, don't you?' he said gently.

Heat flamed in her face, but she nodded, trying to smile.

'Love's like music,' Marc whispered. 'Sometimes you have to improvise, try new variations...'

He rolled back closer, leant over to kiss her, and she gave her mouth up to him openly, passionately, regret in the way she clung.

Marc's hand began to touch her softly, tormentingly; she gave a little gasp of pleasure, her eyes tight shut.

He kissed her neck, her breasts, went on downwards, his mouth warm, brushing, teasing. Annie trembled, a husky moan in her throat as she felt his hair brushing her inner thighs, the moist invasion of his tongue probing the secret places that had resisted him a few moments ago.

Annie had discovered the stranger paths of sensuality; she had lost control of her body's responses, a wild, driving rhythm taking her over, her head turning from side to side, her skin glazed with heat, her mouth open in a low moan as she came towards the cliff edge of satisfaction, trembling and lost to everything but this fierce need.

As the screw turned for that final time she almost lost consciousness, the intensity was so great. Her cries of pleasure went on and on until she slowed and stopped, lay there, like a drowned creature, empty and still and pale.

Marc lay down beside her again. Annie almost went to sleep; she felt she could have slept for a hundred years, like the princess in the fairy-tale, except that there was no thicket of thorns around her, and no spell on her, and the prince was here, on the bed, beside her.

They lay together in silence for a long time, until she roused herself to whisper, 'Thank you.'

'Oh, I enjoyed it, too,' Marc said, laughing huskily.

She turned her face into his chest, her lips apart, warm and moist on his skin. 'Let me do that for you now...'

'Next time, Annie,' he said, his hands playing with her hair. 'I hate to say it, but we don't have the time. We must have breakfast and start out for Paris.'

Her head swung, her green eyes startled. 'At once?'

His smile teased. 'You were desperate to get there yesterday.'

'Was it only yesterday?' She seemed to have been with him forever, and she didn't want to leave.

'Only yesterday,' he gravely said, watching her.

She sighed. 'Time's so strange, isn't it? We haven't even known each other twenty-four hours, and yet I feel I've known you all my life.'

'All our lives,' he corrected, and she did a double take, her heart turning over.

'Oh, Marc... I wish I knew...'

'Whether it was true?' Marc's dark eyes glowed, lustrous, filled with certainty. 'It is, Annie.'

She was afraid of hurting him. Gently she said, 'I know you're sure, but I'm not, although I'm beginning to wish I were. I'd like to believe it, Marc. There's just some very down-to-earth part of me that can't accept it could be true.'

His face stayed calm and assured. 'It doesn't matter any more, Annie. I brought you here because I wanted to convince you we'd known each other before, but now I realise it doesn't matter. All that matters is this moment in time, not any others. If we have lived before, and forgotten our past lives, that was what was intended. To remember would make it very hard to start again, wouldn't it? I may be a freak, an accident—if I really do remember my previous life. But maybe you're right and I'm the victim of my own over-vivid imagination, and a childhood obsession.' He shrugged, his smooth bare shoulders rippling. 'It doesn't matter.'

She leaned over and kissed him softly on the mouth; their lips clung, warm, open, passionate.

As they drew apart, Marc said with a sigh, 'Well, we'd better hurry—you're due to lunch with the managing director of the French record company and some of his executives at one o'clock today, and you have a photo call in the hotel ballroom after that.'

He slid off the bed and picked up a striped gold and black robe from a chair, shrugged into it, and tied the belt around his waist.

Annie was stunned. 'What are you talking about? I don't remember having appointments today—and even if I do, how do you know about them?'

On his way to the bathroom, he coolly said, 'The French record company have a media manager—he set up an agenda for you to meet the Press before the concert. I've seen the schedule that's been sent out to the media, giving all your appointments.'

'How did you get hold of it?' Annie asked, but he just smiled at her over his shoulder as the bathroom door closed on him.

Who was he? she wondered, going back to her own room. What wasn't he telling her? She had realised from the first moment they met that he must have some inside track, a way of finding out very private information about her. He had said he wasn't a journalist, but she was beginning to be certain he was in the media. How

else would he have got hold of the information pack on
her European tour which had been sent out?

She showered, dressed with some care in one of the
outfits Di and Phil had chosen for this tour's meetings
with the Press—like all her stage clothes it was deliberately designed to match her public image as a sad and
lonely waif, a street singer. She never wore the glittering
costumes other singers wore. She came on stage in jeans,
usually black, often barefoot or in old trainers, wearing
a black tank top or sweatshirt. At first she had bought
all her gear off the peg, but now Phil insisted that she
wear outfits created especially for her by a young,
modern London designer. The look was basically the
same, but it had been co-ordinated to make exactly the
right statement, and the designer was making a fortune
these days by selling high street versions of her 'look'
to kids at bargain basement prices.

Today the black top she put on was a midi version,
cut short at the midriff, leaving her waist bare above
black jeans which fitted snugly around the hips, but since
it was quite a cool spring day she decided to wear a white
sweater over her thin black top until it was time to meet
the media.

Marc knocked on the door just as she was dealing
with her hair. 'Coming down to breakfast? I've laid the
table and made the coffee.'

'I have to pack my case again, but I can do that after
breakfast, I suppose,' she said, opening the door. He
was wearing the dark, smoothly tailored suit again, with
a blue and white striped shirt and a dark blue silk tie.
He looked elegant, but the toughness was undisguisable.

'You look wonderful,' he murmured, smiling at her. 'But I thought you always wore just black for photo calls.'

'That's the gimmick Phil dreamed up,' she said, laughing. 'And under this sweater I'm wearing a little black top—I'll slip the sweater off before I meet the Press.'

They had freshly squeezed orange juice, coffee and hot croissants for breakfast. Annie couldn't believe when he opened the oven and took the tray of perfect golden-glazed crescents out, filling the kitchen with a delicious scent of hot pastry.

'You made these?' she incredulously asked.

He laughed. 'I could have done—my mother taught me how—but there wasn't time. I put the oven on as soon as I got downstairs, took half a dozen croissants out of the deep-freeze, and when the oven was the right temperature popped them in; they only take twelve minutes to cook.'

'They're wonderful,' Annie said, taking a bite of flaky, buttery pastry. 'Mmm...I shouldn't eat this—it must be full of calories—but I can't resist. The French do have the best food in the world.'

'I won't argue with that.' Marc grinned at her, sitting down opposite and sipping his juice. 'Tell me what you remember about your father. How did he feel about living in England, instead of France? Didn't he ever want to come back home? He was so very French.'

'Maybe he had thought of it, once, but by the time I was old enough to notice anything he had a good job and was very settled in England.'

'I suppose when you're married, with a family to take care of, you tend to be more careful,' agreed Marc.

She shot him a glance across the table. 'You've never been married?'

'I never met anyone I wanted to marry.'

'But you must have had some relationships over the years. How old are you, by the way?'

His dark eyes teased her. 'I told you that yesterday, have you forgotten? Thirty-four, just ten years older than you are, Annie. And yes, of course I dated women now and then, and I have to admit I slept with several of them, but it was never serious, either for me or them. You can like someone a lot, be very attracted, yet never fall in love, never feel that if you lose them you're going to be badly hurt.'

Annie refilled her coffee-cup, poured some for him too. Frowning, she said, 'I wouldn't really know. I've never had any love-life, except the odd, arranged date with another pop star, which Phil set up, and he made sure that never went any further.'

'He really controls every aspect of your life, doesn't he?' Marc ironically murmured.

Annie grimaced. 'I was so young when we first met that Phil felt he had to keep a close eye on me, protect me. That was why he got Diana to share my flat, go everywhere with me, especially at first. He'd been around the music business all his life; he knew the sort of things that could happen to naïve kids who hit the street without knowing what they were doing. He'd had other young stars who got hooked on drugs or drink, and one who died of Aids. He was determined to keep me safe from all that, and I'm grateful he did now. From time to time I got rebellious and shouted at him over not having enough freedom, but I was so busy most days that I never actually had time to brood over it. And anyway...'

Her voice died away, and Marc watched her, dark eyes narrowing.

'And anyway, you were a little in love with him?' he supplied in a dry voice.

Pink colour flowered in her face. 'I had a crush on him for years,' she admitted. 'I think he took my father's place. I'd always loved my father more than my mother, and I missed him. Phil wasn't like him, but he was protective, and...well, fatherly. I loved that. I was angry with my mother for remarrying so soon after my father died, and I hated my stepfather. He didn't like me much, either. I was a nuisance; I reminded him that he wasn't the first man in my mother's life. He was jealous about that, and because I resented him and argued with him he had an excuse for beating me up every so often.' She grimaced. 'I suppose, to be fair, I was a typical awkward teenager, and could be a pain in some moods. So he could always justify what he did to me, and if I complained to her my mother said it was my own fault.'

His face grave, Marc said, 'You had a bad childhood.'

'Miserable,' she said, pulling a face. 'From the minute my father died, my home life went downhill.'

'Until you met Phil,' he thought aloud, and she nodded.

'Yes. Phil found me just at the right time. God knows what would have happened to me if he hadn't come along. I'd probably have run away from home, lived in London, ended up on the street; it makes me shudder when I think of it.'

Marc took her hand and held it, lifted it to his lips. 'I won't be jealous of Phil, then,' he said lightly.

She gave a husky laugh. 'You don't need to be.'

She heard the intake of his breath, then he looked at the kitchen clock and turned brisk and businesslike again. 'We'll have to be on our way soon. You go up and pack your case again, Annie, while I tidy up in here. I like to leave the place tidy.'

'I'll help,' she said, getting to her feet, but he shook his head.

'I can manage; it won't take me five minutes. Give me a shout when you want me to bring your cases down and put them in the car.'

Annie went upstairs, feeling like a child dragging her feet when she doesn't want to go somewhere.

She didn't want to go back to Paris, back to her busy working life, back to the hurly-burly of publicity, rehearsals, performances, endless travel from one gig to another. Being here had been like stepping out of time, arriving on another planet and seeing the world from an entirely new angle, distanced and with new eyes. So much had happened during the last twenty-four hours; she felt as if she had been away for weeks. Nothing would ever be the same for her, she was certain of that.

Slowly she packed her case, looked around the bedroom, remembering with a shock her feelings when she first saw it. She spent some time tidying up, stripped the bed, put the sheets into the bathroom linen basket.

'Are you ready, Annie?' Marc called from downstairs.

'Yes, OK,' she said huskily, and he ran up to collect her cases and take them out to the car, which was now parked right outside the house. By the time she joined him Marc had stowed her luggage and was waiting for her.

'Do you want to ride in the back in stately isolation, or will you sit in front with me?' he teased.

She made a face at him and got into the front. As they drove away she looked back over her shoulder, a long sigh wrenching her.

Without looking at her, Marc said softly, 'You'll see it again.'

'Oh, you can read the future, as well as the past?' she mocked him, and he grinned.

'I hope so.'

Annie's heart turned over. It was at that instant that she knew she hoped they had a future, too. There was so much against them. The way she felt might not last, his obsession with her might fade now he had really got to know her, her career might whirl them apart and keep them away from each other until their feelings withered and died... Anything could happen. She was afraid to be too optimistic. Yet hope glowed inside her like a light in darkness. She didn't want to stop feeling this way. She was happier than she had ever been in her life before. Every time she looked sideways there he was, driving the car, his profile carved and intent, tanned skin stretched over austere bone-structure, lids half down over those glittering dark eyes, his mouth a warm, relaxed line. Annie got the same stab of feeling every time. She wanted to laugh out loud; joy bubbled through her veins. She felt she could fly, if she tried.

'Tell me some more about your childhood,' she murmured. 'Is it cold in the winter, in the Jura?'

'It certainly can be! Some winters there's snow on the ground for weeks on end,' Marc said, smiling. 'I used to love winter when I was a boy; we all did. There was always so much to do—skating, skiing, tobogganing. Boys were always getting their front teeth knocked out, or turning up at school on Monday with black eyes or a broken arm. I never understood why my parents used to complain about the snow; I thought they were spoilsports.'

'I expect your mother worried about you.'

'I'm sure she did. She was very family-orientated. In fact, she wasn't interested in anything else. She spent most of her day in the house and garden; she was a great gardener. She didn't grow many flowers; she preferred vegetables. A very practical woman, my mother.'

'And she taught you to cook?'

He nodded. 'When she had time and I was around. I was more often out with my friends, playing rugby, fighting, climbing trees.'

'She was a great cook?'

'Oh, yes. She insisted on the best ingredients... everything fresh, preferably grown by herself. She had a little herb garden, and a small orchard—she rarely bought fruit or vegetables in the market, even in winter. I often used to be sent out to bring in winter cabbage for dinner, on days when I had to dig for it in deep snow. My fingers would be freezing by the time I got back to the house.'

Annie didn't notice time passing. She was too interested in what Marc was telling her about his childhood, his family, the life in the Jura mountains and valleys. It sounded warm, romantic, a wonderful life, and she was aching to get there and see the place for herself. She had a deep sense now that she would feel she was going home when she did.

Suddenly she saw a road sign and realised they would soon be in Paris; and at once she got jittery, her nerves on edge. Marc had said that her absence wouldn't be noticed, that nobody would look for her, but she couldn't help wondering if he was right. What if Phil and Di had rung up, or someone from the French recording company had been in touch, only to discover that she wasn't at the hotel, had never even checked in, was, in fact, missing? She could imagine the panic and uproar that would have caused.

What if Marc was arrested as soon as they arrived? She shot him a look, chewing her lower lip.

'Marc, maybe you should drop me somewhere, instead of taking me to the hotel. I can get a taxi.'

He gave her a warm, amused look. 'Why on earth should I do that?'

'The police might be swarming all over the hotel!'

'They won't be.'

'Marc!' she began in agitation, but he just put a hand out, patted her knee.

'Stop worrying. I told you, everyone believes you've been staying with friends.'

They drove into the chaos of Paris traffic, the storm of cars whirling around them so fiercely that Annie kept shutting her eyes, terrified. There was a continuous blare of hooting; tyres screeched. Cars swerved past, almost hitting them, the drivers leaning out to bellow hoarse insults in French. She was glad she never had to drive in these conditions, but Marc didn't turn a hair, as if he was totally used to it, drove here every day.

Maybe he did she thought, frowning.

'Do you live in Paris?' That was one thing he hadn't touched on as he talked about his background. He had told her all about the past, nothing about his present.

'All week. On Friday evening I usually head for the country.'

Her eyes widened. 'Was that your house we just came from?' She had been sure he had rented it for a week or so.

'Yes,' he said coolly. 'I spend weekends and summer holidays there; I prefer life in the country, but I need to spend the weeks in town, because my work keeps me very busy until quite late each day.'

'You still haven't told me what work you do!'

'Later,' he said, slowing as they drove along a wide boulevard lined with smart shops. A moment later he turned into a narrower street and pulled up outside one of Paris's grand hotels. A uniformed porter hurried to welcome them, came round to open Annie's door and help her out.

Marc tossed him the car keys, smiled, and said in French, 'Park the car for me, would you, please, Jean-Pierre? And see that Mademoiselle Dumont's luggage is taken up to her suite.'

The porter nodded, smiling cheerfully. '*Bien sûr, Monsieur Pascal.*'

Annie registered with a little shock that the man knew Marc well. Marc was clearly a frequent client, which meant that he must have quite a bit of money. This was an expensive hotel.

A second later another, bigger shock hit her as she realised where she had heard the name Pascal before. It had come up a number of times in recent conversations with Phil and Di. Marc Pascal was the managing director of the French recording company who put out her discs. She had come back to Paris to have lunch with Marc himself!

CHAPTER EIGHT

'I DIDN'T tell you who I was because I wanted to crash through all the usual barriers,' Marc said a little while later, when they were alone again, in her elegant top floor suite with a breathtaking view of Paris from every window.

'Well, you did that all right!' Annie muttered, glowering at him.

He sighed. 'If you had known from the start that you were perfectly safe you wouldn't have listened to a word I said. You'd have laughed at me, thought it was all a big joke. I had to give you a shock, Annie, focus your mind, if I was to make you receptive to my story.'

'Brainwash me, you mean!'

His black eyes flashed. 'No, Annie. That isn't true! I couldn't think of another way of reaching you. I didn't know whether or not you had any memories of a past life, but you looked exactly like your grandmother, like the woman I kept dreaming about. When I first saw a picture of you it nearly made my heart stop.'

Her own heart turned over violently at the way he looked at her, the note in his voice.

Huskily he said, 'For a long time, believe me, I'd wondered if I was just imagining this woman in my dreams; I'd never seen any photos of your grandmother, you see. I didn't know for sure that the Annie I dreamed about was the same Anna Dumont who had once lived in my village. I'd asked around, I'd tried to check up, but nobody seemed to remember her very well. A few old women did, but they were very vague. I was certainly never told she had anything to do with the dead airman in the village cemetery. Then I saw a picture of you and realised you had the same name, and of course I wondered . . . could you be her granddaughter? I knew she had gone to England after the war, and when I found out that your father's name had been Pierre Dumont I was certain who you were, but a strong family resemblance didn't mean you were the same woman reborn.'

'No, it doesn't!' she quickly said. 'I'm glad you do realise that, Marc!'

'I'm as rational as you are, Annie; I'm not crazy,' he drily said. 'But you know what Shakespeare says in Hamlet: "There are more things in heaven and earth, Horatio, than are dreamt of in your philosophy". However incredible it seems, it is possible. It seemed to me that, if I was a reincarnation of that Englishman, why shouldn't the woman he loved be somewhere in the world? I just had to find her, and after I'd seen pictures of you I knew I had to find out if there was more than just a physical resemblance.' He paused, his mouth twisting in self-mockery. 'I suppose I secretly hoped you might have had the same dreams.'

'Well, I didn't,' she said coldly, still angry with him for frightening the life out of her by making her think she had been kidnapped, when all the time her stay at his country home had been arranged in advance with Phil's office. Marc had told her coolly that she hadn't been informed because it was planned as a 'surprise' for her when she got to Paris. It had certainly been that, and it would be a long time before Annie got over the surprise.

'But you have now,' he said softly, and she gave him a hard glance.

'Why don't you admit you hypnotised me? Those dreams I had at your house...you planted them in my head, and before you woke me up you told me to forget I'd ever been hypnotised, didn't you?'

'No, Annie,' he broke out fiercely. 'That isn't true.'

'I don't believe you! Why should I? You pulled the wool over my eyes when you made me think you'd kidnapped me. How do I know you aren't lying about those dreams?'

'Hypnotising you into believing me would have been a pointless exercise,' Marc said in a deep, angry voice. 'I needed to know if you were the woman I had loved before. I took you into the country alone with me to set up the conditions I thought might trigger off any memory you did have... Why on earth would I cheat, by hypnotising you?'

'You've admitted how much you wanted to believe I was my own grandmother, born again. You were obsessed. You'd have done anything to make me believe I was her, wouldn't you?'

'You're wrong, Annie,' he said deeply. 'I wanted you to be her—but only if you really were!'

They stared at each other fixedly, Annie's green eyes accusing, bright with rage, Marc's dark gaze insistent, compelling.

'And if I wasn't?' she whispered. 'What then? You'd have lost interest, I suppose.'

The telephone rang. They both started, the noise breaking the mood. Scowling, Marc turned abruptly and snatched the phone up.

'Yes?' he snarled.

Annie was trembling so much that she had to sit down on the nearest chair. She still hadn't got over the surprise of finding out Marc's real identity and realising the charade he had been playing for her benefit over the last twenty-four hours. She couldn't remember when she had ever felt this angry before. She felt he had made a fool of her.

To take her mind off her feelings, she forced herself to look about her, appraising the sitting-room of the luxury suite she would be occupying during her stay in Paris. It was charmingly furnished, in Empire style, with green satin brocade chairs and sofas, a pale yellow carpet, wallpaper printed with elegant scrollwork on a cream background. A chandelier hung from the centre of the ceiling, elaborate cascades of glass droplets tinkling every time someone walked around the room. Long green satin brocade curtains hung at the windows, which ran almost from the ceiling to the floor, tied back at the moment with silken gold cords.

Marc put the phone down with a crash and Annie stiffened, her head turning towards him again.

'We're expected downstairs,' he said curtly. 'My people have arrived and are in the bar, waiting. We want to get lunch over in good time, before you have to face the cameras.'

'You go down. I need to do something about my make-up and hair.'

'No, I'll wait.' He looked at his watch. 'Five minutes, Annie, that's all you've got. Hurry up.'

Her teeth clamped together. Without a word she got up and walked into the bathroom, aware of him watching her, violently conscious of him every second of the time, and bitterly angry with herself for that. Any attraction she had believed she felt had to be suspect now. He had planned it all so carefully, gone to such lengths to deceive her.

As he himself had said, he had intended her to be 'receptive' to what he told her. How did she know just how far he had been prepared to go?

Her imagination came up with wild ideas of mind-changing drugs, subliminal interference, if not hypnosis itself.

Oh, it was crazy! she told herself, brushing her long, silky black hair and winding it up again into a sleek chignon at the back of her head. Every explanation she came up with seemed too unbelievable to be true.

But something had to account for the instant attraction she had felt from the minute she set eyes on him. She'd never had anything like that happen to her before. It was true that she hadn't dated many men in the past, but she had met plenty of them, on tour with her band, and when she was recording. Nobody had ever hit her like an avalanche before.

Yet Marc had. Even when they were driving towards Paris, that first day, before he so much as said a word to her, she had felt a strong physical attraction. She remembered sitting there staring at his black hair and olive skin, the wide shoulders, the dark eyes, thinking that he was one of the best-looking men she had seen in a long time.

She'd never been that struck by anyone before, and as for what was to happen later... Hot crimson colour flowed up under her skin as she looked at herself in the mirror, remembering the way they had made love, in the wood, in the bedroom. She shut her eyes, groaning. How could she have let that happen? She couldn't even

comfort herself by saying he had used any sort of co-
ercion. She had wanted him; her mouth went dry as she
admitted she still did. How had that happened to her?
She'd have sworn she wasn't the type to go overboard
for a complete stranger, be ready to go to bed with him
only hours after meeting him.

She didn't know how Marc had done it, but if this
had been another century she would be accusing him of
putting a spell on her!

She delicately brushed silvery green eyeshadow over
her lids, renewed her glossy red lipstick, considered her
reflection with her head to one side, sighed. That would
have to do. She would obviously get another chance to
do her make-up before the photographers arrived for
the picture opportunity. First she had to have lunch with
Marc and his executives, and that was going to be nerve-
racking enough.

She emerged from the pale lemon and green tiled
bathroom to find Marc pacing up and down the room
impatiently, that lean, powerful body vibrating with
tension.

He swung, his tanned face grim.

'Oh, there you are! I was beginning to wonder if you
were planning to stay in there all day!'

She had taken off her white sweater and was now
wearing the outfit Phil had picked out for her to wear
for her first meeting with the media. Marc's narrowed
gaze absorbed it, his black brows jerking together in a
jagged line as he took in her plunging neckline, which
revealed the deep valley between her breasts and the beginning of the round, smooth-skinned breasts themselves. The black top clung to her like a second skin,

but ended just above the midriff, leaving a bare expanse of pale skin.

'Is that what you're wearing?'

'Obviously!' she retorted, lifting her chin, her green eyes defiant. 'Don't you like it? The band thought it was very sexy.'

'I'm sure they did,' he said through his teeth. He looked at his watch, his forehead still corrugated. 'Well, there isn't time to look for something else. Come on, we'd better go, but I'll take a look at the other outfits you're planning to wear. We've been selling you over here as a sad little street singer; you've never had a sexy image.'

'Maybe I haven't in the past, but I think I will have in future,' she said aggressively.

Marc threw her a barbed look, black eyes glittering. 'Oh, do you? We'll talk about that later.' He threw open the door of the suite, and gestured. 'Come on, we're going to be late!'

She was in a mood to be annoying. She took her time swaying past him, not even glancing his way, her expression as calm and contained as she could make it, although she was very conscious of Marc staring at her, even more aware of the rigidity and tension of his body.

They made an odd couple; Annie caught sight of them both in the polished wood of the lift door. Herself in her sexy black top and sleek, tight-fitting black jeans; Marc looking authoritative, not to say autocratic, very formal and remote, in that elegantly tailored dark suit.

It was hard to associate what she knew about his dream world with the man standing beside her in the lift as they went down to the ground floor. Anyone seeing him from outside would be struck immediately by his good looks, his physical power, the hard bone-structure and the restless energy. Nobody would suspect that Marc was the type to believe in reincarnation or take any note of his dreams, let alone have such a complex and unusual mind. He looked so conventional, so sure of himself and his lifestyle.

If I'd met him today, looking like that, I'd have flipped over him! thought Annie as they walked out of the lift into the busy ground floor of the hotel. He didn't have to put me through that bizarre mock-kidnap just to get my attention. He must know what an effect he has on women.

Of course, it would have taken a lot longer to get to the same point in their relationship. She had to admit he was right there. If they were meeting today for the first time, they wouldn't be alone; they would have Marc's executives at lunch with them. And within another day or so Annie would be fully engaged in Press and publicity interviews, rehearsals, sound checks and all the paraphernalia of getting ready for a performance. And when she had done the Paris gig she would have moved on to the next venue, with the whole circus of musicians, backing singers, tour workers. She wouldn't have the time to see Marc, and he wouldn't have been able to get very close, make any deep or lasting impression.

A few people in the hotel foyer had suddenly recognised her; she heard the hush, then whispering broke out. People stared; a handful of them began hurrying towards her.

'Oh, dear,' she said helplessly, trying to recall a little French, in case she had to talk to people.

'What?' Marc asked, then followed the direction of her gaze and grunted. 'We haven't got time for fans; they'll just get in the way. Come on.'

He put an arm around her and rushed her away, through the doors of the hotel dining-room, saying drily to the head waiter as he met them,

'Anton, we're being chased. Keep them out, would you?'

The head waiter gave an unsurprised, soothing smile. *'Bien sûr, Monsieur Pascal.'*

While Annie and Marc walked across the dining-room to a large table by the window, looking out into a courtyard garden, the head waiter moved to intercept a couple of the bolder spirits of those on their trail, saying firmly but politely, 'Unless you are booked in for lunch, I'm afraid you cannot come in here!'

'Salut!' Marc said to the half a dozen people seated at the table, who all hurriedly got to their feet, smiling, answering him.

'Salut.'

'Bonjour.'

Several even said, 'Hi!' but with strong French accents.

They were busy inspecting Annie, too. She was used to being stared at by now, but she still found it a bit of a problem. Her colour rose; she had butterflies in her stomach. She would have liked to turn tail and bolt back to her bedroom. She was not so much shy as self-conscious, afraid of being a disappointment. People had such fixed ideas about you; they expected you to be miraculous, a cross between a saint and a raving beauty. The sun was supposed to shine out of you. And Annie knew she was very ordinary: a little, skinny girl with long black hair and sometimes mournful green eyes. The only thing about her that was not ordinary was her voice. She could sing. That was her one gift; it had changed her life. She was grateful to God every day for giving her that voice.

'Well, here she is,' Marc said lightly, his arm still round her.

Could he feel the tremor running through her? she wondered, and didn't dare risk meeting his eyes.

He introduced his staff one by one. 'This is Raoul, head of A and R.'

Annie shook hands with the short young man who headed the most vital area of any recording company, the artist and repertoire department. Raoul could be her age, and looked, she thought, rather like a very young Napoleon: olive skin, black hair cut with a fringe, a slightly full face, but an aggressive chin. But he wore very modern clothes: Jean Paul Gaultier, she suspected, from the extreme styling. He must be earning a good salary!

'These two are his chief talent-spotters,' Marc briskly said. 'Simone and Gerard.'

They were even younger, the girl about twenty-two, with a tousled bob of black hair and dark eyes. The boy was any age between eighteen and twenty-five, skinny, serious, and also dark-eyed and dark-haired. They both wore black trousers, black shirts, pink ties. They looked like twins.

'Spotted any great new talent recently?' asked Annie cheerfully.

They shrugged. Looked at each other. Shook their heads, unworried by their admission.

'We look at a lot of people every week...' Simone said.

'But almost never find anyone really new, or different,' said Gerard.

'Well, you must know how it is,' said Simone.

'It's a tough business to break into,' said Gerard.

Annie wondered if they went around together all the time, talked in unison—it was an act, carefully worked out, she decided, amused.

She said, 'I had a lucky break right at the start, or I wouldn't be here today.'

They both nodded. 'Right!' they said in English in unison.

'This is Francine,' Marc said, moving her along to meet the last two guests, who were from the marketing department. 'She's the head of the art department; she's responsible for the covers on your French recordings, so if you have any complaints about them she's the one to make them to!'

The tall, long-legged blonde girl laughed, but her blue eyes were frosty.

'I hope you don't have any complaints,' she quickly warned Annie.

'None,' Annie said, knowing she wouldn't have dared voice them if she had, not faced with that expression. 'The French covers are gorgeous.'

Francine thawed a little. 'Thank you. We think so. I've just seen your new logo—I love it, by the way.' She looked down at the fat folder on the table in front of her. 'I think it's gorgeous; especially against the black.'

The cover of the folder was black; Annie's official logo stood out brilliantly against it—an embossed pair of slanting green eyes, cat-like, naughty, with a fringe of thick black lashes.

'I thought it was silly when they first put the idea up,' confessed Annie, 'but my manager loved it.'

'We all do, too,' Francine assured her.

The logo was going on all her publicity releases and on the backs of records. It was the most recent development from the English recording company's image department, who had been working on a logo for her for months before settling for this one. Successful recording stars mostly had a logo these days, a simple symbol which would tell fans at a glance, without needing words, that a record was by her, or an article about her.

The last of the executives turned out to be the head of publicity for the company, Louis, a very elegant young man who at once started telling Annie some of his plans for the French part of the tour.

The head waiter appeared. 'If you are ready, *monsieur*, may we begin serving?'

'Yes, right away.' Marc nodded, and held a chair back for Annie to sit down between himself and Raoul, the head of A and R.

'We ordered the meal beforehand, as there were quite a few of us, to save time,' Marc told her. 'If there's anything you don't like we can always order you something else. I asked your people in London if there was any food you hated to eat, but they couldn't think of anything.'

'I eat most things,' she agreed.

The first course was terrine of rabbit and prunes, served with toasted brioche, a sprinkling of pickled gherkins, sliced tomatoes and spring onions with crisp lettuce.

'Delicious,' Annie said to Marc's lifted eyebrow of enquiry, and he smiled.

'We eat it all the time in the Jura.'

'That's where Marc comes from,' Raoul told her, and she nodded.

'So he keeps saying.'

Raoul laughed. 'He's very proud of the place. Have you ever been there?'

Annie shook her head, avoiding Marc's sideways glance, the glinting amusement in his eyes.

'Neither have I, but Marc makes it sound like the outskirts of paradise.' Raoul laughed loudly; Marc didn't.

'Where do you come from?' asked Annie.

'I'm a Parisian.' Raoul's tone made it clear he felt it was far better to have been born in Paris than in the Jura.

'You have to understand,' said Marc drily, 'that France is two countries. Paris, and the rest. You are either a Parisian, or a Frenchman; they're not necessarily the same thing.'

Raoul laughed loudly again, appearing to accept this entirely. 'But we're very cosmopolitan,' he drawled. 'We eat the best of French provincial cooking in Paris.'

'Even *poulet au vin jaune*,' Marc said, as the waiter removed their plates and a heated trolley was wheeled towards them, loaded with food. 'This next dish is another speciality from the Jura—chicken, cooked in the yellow wine of the Jura region, with cream and *morilles*, a dark brown honeycomb-like fungus. The variety that grows in the Jura pine forests near my village has the best flavour, in my opinion.'

Raoul winked at her and Annie laughed, watching her portion of *poulet au vin jaune* being spooned on to a warm plate, to which was added boiled wild rice faintly coloured with saffron, and French *petite pois*, cooked with fragments of lettuce and onion.

Marc said softly to her, 'If you can't come to the Jura, I thought I'd bring the Jura to you.'

Her pulses leapt as she met his dark-eyed stare, the intent, intimate gaze which rarely left her.

Had any of the others noticed the way he kept watching her, the way his voice changed every time he spoke to her? She hoped they hadn't. It was a relief to be sure that they couldn't know that under the table he kept moving his knee against hers, that every so often his hand would brush lightly over her fingers, her arm, her thigh.

The tiny contacts made her breathless, made her heartbeat quicken, her mouth go dry, but she wished he wouldn't. She still didn't know what to think about him, what to make of what he had been telling her. She needed time to work out exactly what was happening inside her. He mustn't rush her any more. He had already rushed her quite enough.

She couldn't say any of that to him, though, over lunch with all those strangers around the table, listening, watching.

She moved her knee away from his, pushed his hand down, avoided touching him whenever she could, but her tactics simply seemed to amuse Marc, whose dark eyes glinted teasingly whenever she met them.

After lunch, Louis and Marc escorted her to meet the Press. Annie was used to being photographed by now, but it was still always exhausting, not to mention boring, being treated like a living doll, pushed and pulled into different positions, asked to smile, turn her head this way and that, to sit here and there.

She was relieved at being released from all that and allowed to go up to her suite to rest. Marc came with her, but stayed in the sitting-room of the suite, making quiet telephone calls in a very low voice, while Annie locked herself into her bedroom and lay down on the bed, closing her eyes with a sigh of relief.

It only seemed like five minutes later that she heard loud ringing from the front door of the suite, then Marc running to answer it, yanking the door open and muttering angrily, 'Stop ringing that bell!' Then his voice changed. 'Oh! It's you!'

Annie wasn't asleep. Not any more. Yawning, she listened, and then snapped wide awake as she heard Phil's voice.

'Tired already, is she? And we haven't even started yet! I hope this isn't going to be one of those tours! Well, never mind... Hi, Marc, how are you? Everything OK so far? Any problems? No? Good. You haven't met my wife, have you? Diana, this is Marc Pascal, the MD of the French recording company.'

Annie almost fell off the bed, running to unlock her bedroom door, and burst out just as Marc ushered the new arrivals into the suite. Diana and Phil looked round, smiling.

'There you are! What's all this about you being tired before we even hit the road?' scolded Phil, his eyes skating over her. 'I hope you haven't been burning the candle at both ends while we've been away. Let's look at you!' He kissed her on both cheeks, took her hands, assessed her with those cynical blue eyes, his head to one side. 'Hmm... you look different, somehow! Or maybe it's just that we haven't seen you for a couple of weeks. Have you been OK?'

'Fine,' she said, laughing. 'I'm a big girl now, Phil. I managed just fine on my own.' She turned to hug Diana. 'You've both got such great tans! It's wonderful to see you both. How's married life, Di? Do you think it will ever catch on?'

'So far so good,' said Di, her brown eyes warm and glowing. 'At least he doesn't snore. How does it feel to have the flat to yourself? It wasn't too lonely, was it?' Her voice was light, but Annie saw the faint anxiety in her eyes, and smiled reassurance, shaking her head.

'It felt a bit odd at first, but I'm enjoying being independent. No more arguments about what to watch on TV! And I don't have to turn my music down, either!'

Diana laughed. 'I can see there are going to be complaints from the neighbours!'

'Do you think this hotel can produce a good pot of tea?' Phil asked, wandering into the sitting-room, and they all followed him.

Marc looked doubtful, wrinkled his nose. 'Tea? I imagine they often get asked for it by English visitors, but whether they make it well or not I wouldn't like to guess.' He picked up the phone. 'Tea . . . for how many? Two? How about you, Annie?'

'I'll have tea, too.' She nodded.

Di watched him make the call to Room Service. She whispered in Annie's ear, 'Now he's what I call sexy. Didn't he take you to visit his country house? What was it like?'

What on earth was she supposed to say in answer to that? Annie swallowed and tried, 'Remote; a peaceful sort of place.'

'Is he married?'

Annie shook her head, and got a sharper, more curious look from Diana.

'Who else was staying there, then?'

Annie's nerves prickled. She should have realised that question was bound to be asked, sooner or later. Marc was putting down the phone; he caught the plea for help she silently threw him, and came over to join her and Di, saying blandly, 'Is she telling you about my friends? They were all dying to meet Annie; I had a problem keeping the numbers down.'

Diana frowned. 'I thought it was supposed to be a restful break for her, before she began the tour.'

'Oh, I made sure she had plenty of rest. I have a big stake in the success of this tour, remember? We're hoping to sell a lot of discs during the next week or two, and make our fortunes. She already has a big following over here, but I'm certain she's going to be a very big star by the time this tour is over.'

Diana was distracted, as he intended; she smiled delightedly. 'Of course she is! And not just in France—all over Europe.' She put an arm round Annie and hugged her. 'Aren't you?'

Annie laughed. 'Let's hope so!' But she was thinking, Oh, Marc was convincing, cool as a cucumber, covering up the truth without a blink. Watching that display of mental sleight of hand had made her wonder just what sort of man he was! How much truth had he ever told her, for a start?

Marc watched her, his eyes hard, probing her face. She realised he was trying to read her mind, tune into her mood, work out what she was feeling.

Phil and Diana's arrival had changed everything, and he had picked up on that, no doubt. Their return had called her back into the warm, familiar circle of their long-time relationship, split her off from Marc, made her deeply aware of how short a time she had known him, how little she knew about him, compared to the length and closeness of her friendship with Di and Phil.

Alone with Marc for hours, she had had no polite public mask to wear, no armour of social manners or pretences to hide behind. She had had to face him as herself, unadorned, stripped to the bone of her own nature, the woman she really was, not the layers of acquired personality written about in newspapers, talked about by disc jockeys, gossiped about by fans. That Annie had been largely invented by the media and her record company's image-builders and was nothing like the real Annie.

She suddenly realised that she probably knew herself better now, after twenty-four hours alone with Marc, than she had ever done in her life before.

It was so easy to start believing your own publicity, so easy to forget how much of your public persona was invention, or exaggeration.

For years she had been kept too busy to think about the increasing split between her real self and the mask put on her face by her media people. When she was seventeen they had answered questions for her, made up answers that suited the image they had for her. Annie had never argued about it. She never had the time, in fact. When could she ever stop and think, Who am I? What do I really think? How do I really feel?

She had opened her mouth and said the words Phil and Diana told her to say. She wore clothes they chose. She went to places they thought she should be seen at— nightclubs, restaurants, hotels, resorts. She had never resented being manipulated, treated like a living doll; she had been only too happy to please them both. She owed them both so much, after all; and she was fond of them, grateful to them.

But all the same, it was time now that she started running her own life, did her own thinking, made her own decisions.

Marc had helped her see that—which made it all the more ironic that the first thing she decided for herself was never to let him get too near her again.

She stared back at him, her green eyes glittering with defiance—and let him see what she was thinking, said to him silently across the room, Stay away from me, Marc. It's over. I don't believe you and I never want to see you again.

CHAPTER NINE

THAT first gig, in Paris, was a sell-out. Annie hadn't thought she was big enough in France yet to make that sort of impact, but Marc and his media people had done a tremendous job for months in advance creating the right atmosphere, an awareness of her that had been built up until the tour began, with Press hand-outs, constant gossip items placed in the right newspapers and magazines, on cable and satellite TV, posters pasted up in public places, but more especially, of course, interviews with her given out to the music and fan magazines.

'You haven't been out of the media for weeks past,' Louis, the PR guy from the record company, told her with satisfaction and an obvious sense of pride in his own achievement. 'Tickets sold out within days of the box office opening. I think this tour is going to be a smash hit, and France isn't the easiest market for foreign singers, as you know. We have too many great bands of our own. I must admit, I didn't expect to do this well with a first tour.'

'You've done a terrific job!' Annie congratulated him, and he grinned, well pleased with the compliment.

'Thanks. I'll be with you all the time, throughout the tour, to cope with any problems that come up, so don't hesitate to be in touch if you need me.'

'I won't,' she promised, aware that Phil or one of his staff would deal with any problems, anyway. She never had to bother with problems that came up, thank heavens.

She was up at crack of dawn, had a light Continental breakfast, and drove out to the stadium to start rehearsing early on the day of the gig itself.

The sound stage was largely built by then, although a few last-minute hammerings were going on, and men were crawling up and down the steel struts, tightening connections, checking for safety. There had been occasions when a stage fell apart under the gyrations of a big band, or seating collapsed when fans stampeded. Nobody wanted that this time!

Below the stage electricians were busily working away too, testing their circuits. Microphone leads festooned the air; from the mikes themselves came the occasional crackle or buzz as someone tested them.

A band of large, muscular young men had begun humping the instruments into place. Keyboards and drums took up a lot of room, and there were massive amplifiers littering the stage already. Every so often someone would drop something and a loud crash would echo and re-echo in the stadium.

'Watch it!' the guy in charge of the roadies would bellow. 'That stuff costs money!'

'Sorry, Jack!' the offending roadie would mumble, or mutter sulkily, 'He tripped me up!'

'Where's this going?' someone else would shout, and Jack would shout back.

The little group of backing singers stood in front of a row of mikes to the back of the stage, rehearsing, stopping, doing it again.

Annie, her band and the dancers who had joined them now began practising their moves; every movement they would be making on stage had all been planned down to the tiniest detail by a stage choreographer, and rehearsed back in London, in a big hall. Now they had to transfer those moves to the great, open-air stage on which they would perform, taking care not to trip over trailing electric wires or fall off the edge of the stage.

The band was largely static: they would be pinned down by their electronic instruments, taking just a few steps this way, a few back again. Annie could move about far more, and would be going on and off throughout the evening, and all of her moves had had to be planned and rehearsed. The dancers had elaborate routines to perform, sweeping back and forth across the stage like a glittering tide.

While the choreography rehearsals went on the electricians began their lights checks—counting down through the various changes of lighting for the evening, making sure all the circuits were working.

'It's a madhouse,' Brick said to Annie, grinning with enjoyment. 'Don't you love the build-up to a gig? I can feel it working down through me to my toes...'

'What?' she absently asked, watching the dancers flash past, arms whirling, leaping high.

'The adrenalin, stupid!'

'You never get stage fright, do you, Brick?' Annie envied him his cheerful exuberance.

'Not on your life! I can't wait to get out there tonight!' He made drumming gestures, eyes bright. 'Once we get going and the drums are building up I get so excited I feel I could fly if I tried. A live performance is the one time you can drum as hard as you like, and make all the noise you like, without worrying about anyone complaining, or being asked to turn it down! Drumming is like good sex; you can't have too much of it, but other people are always trying to stop you getting it or enjoying it.'

The band thought that very funny. Annie wasn't listening; she was watching Marc talking to Phil at the other end of the stage. The two men were staring up at the heavy lights arranged in batteries overhead. A man on a crane was busy adjusting them, while a man beside him took instructions on a walkie-talkie in his hand from a man standing down on the stage.

Marc was wearing a black sweater and blue jeans; he somehow managed to make the casual gear look elegant and very sexy.

Mouth dry, Annie looked away. She must not let him catch her watching him. She had managed to keep out of his way for the last few days, and once tonight's gig was over she and her circus would be moving on to do the next gig, in Lyon. He would hardly go with them.

The long day wore on; she was getting tired now. She had been on her feet for most of the day; her energy was running down.

'Go and take your rest. You're coming apart,' Di said, putting an arm round her as she broke off in the middle of a rather ragged version of one of her most popular songs.

'That was terrible!' she agreed, grimacing. 'I lost it halfway through. I'd better take it again before I go off.'

'Stop right now, Annie!' bellowed Phil from the seating at the front of the stadium.

She looked round, and as she caught sight of Phil below, with Marc standing next to him, the electricians turned on the full battery of lights in the fading afternoon light, and Annie was blinded by the flash.

For a second she was transfixed, dazzled, in her ears the rattle of machine-guns, the sound of a woman screaming.

'Good God, Annie! What the hell's wrong?' Di broke out from somewhere, invisible to her at that instant while her eyes were filled with all that watt power.

'Get those lights off!' Marc yelled from down below.

The electricians hurried to obey. The lights went out. Darkness seemed to come down.

Annie stood there, shuddering, tears in her eyes. Diana put both arms round her, rubbing her shoulders and back instinctively, murmuring puzzled reassurance.

'OK, OK, I'm here... You're safe... What was it?'

Marc had leapt up on to the stage; over Di's shoulder Annie looked into his face and saw the understanding in his dark eyes, the awareness of what had happened to her just now, what she had seen, heard, experienced.

She quivered, closing her eyes against him.

'Take her back to the hotel,' Phil said quietly to Diana. 'She's out of it. We should have sent her off a couple of hours ago; she's been pushing past the limit. Give her some hot milk and a couple of aspirin, then put her to bed in a dark room. No noise, no TV, no music. Stay in the next room; you can rest on the sofa, but don't go to sleep.'

'I'll take her,' Marc said, and Phil and Di looked at him in amazement.

Diana smiled politely. 'That's kind of you, but that's my job. I look after Annie.'

Marc didn't argue, but Annie felt the vibrations of his impatience with them.

'Let's go,' Diana said, steering her off stage, her arm around her. Annie was glad to get away from Marc's

dark gaze. Would she have had that flash of vision if
he hadn't been there, watching her, willing her to
remember?

Back in her hotel room she slept heavily, a sleep punc-
tuated by dreams from which she woke now and then,
dazed, shuddering, not remembering where she was for
an instant as she stared around the strange, dark
bedroom, only to fall back and slip straight into sleep
again.

She was exhausted. Even bad dreams couldn't stop
her sleeping. Perhaps she was having bad dreams because she was so tired she wondered, hovering on the
cloudy edge of sleep.

Diana woke her up with a cup of tea in good time to
dress and get ready to drive back to the stadium. They
were going in a caterer's van. The fans might not notice
that slipping past the chanting ring around the stadium
entrances, and, even if they did, they wouldn't see Annie
inside; the windows had been blacked out.

'Food?' asked Di.

She shook her head, stomach heaving.

'Ought to eat a sandwich,' Di said, unsurprised, but
still trying to persuade her, for once, to eat before a
concert, knowing she never did, couldn't keep food
down.

'Don't even talk about it! Let's go!'

They got past the crowds without anyone suspecting
a thing, and Annie was bundled out of the van down a
private entry which led to the dressing-rooms far below,
in the maze of rooms and passages under the stadium.
She found the band sitting about looking edgy and pale;
only Brick was cheerful. A roadie brought him a vast
hamburger while he was talking to Annie. The lead

guitarist looked at Brick's mouth opening, the wedge of food going in, and dashed for the bathroom.

'You've got no nerves!' Annie accused Brick, averting her own eyes from the sight of his jaws.

'I'm hungry. I've been working like a dog,' he justified.

'You're always hungry!' the others in the band chorused, throwing magazines, old shoes, a couple of books, at him.

He ducked, chuckling. 'Collection of mental cripples, the lot of you!'

'Nervous, honey?' asked Phil, coming up to kiss Annie.

'Petrified.'

'Once you're out there you'll be fine, you know that!' he comforted, and she grimaced, hearing a full-throated roar from up above in the stadium, which was now pulsating with a full audience and the metallic twang of guitars, crashing of drums, from the French band which had gone on first.

'I know. Doesn't help. I haven't got butterflies in my stomach; I've got man-eating tigers.' She glared at Brick, now starting on some shoe-string fries. 'And it doesn't help to have the human garbage muncher over there eating his way through Paris. I'm shocked that the French have junk food like the rest of us. I thought they had better taste.'

'They make great hamburgers!' Brick happily told her.

'Probably made of horse!' the lead guitarist viciously said.

Brick looked horrified. 'You're kidding. They don't eat horses, do they?'

Everyone nodded. Brick turned green.

Phil laughed. 'Well, not long to wait, darling. The warm-up guys are doing a great job, getting them ready for you.' He looked at his watch. 'Another few minutes and the band can go up, then you can follow on when you get your cue.'

Annie dashed into the bathroom, sweat on her forehead. She didn't throw up, but she had to splash cold water on the back of her neck before the turmoil in her stomach calmed down. She stayed in there for a while, working on her make-up, until someone knocked on her door.

'Annie?'

She tensed. It was Marc's voice. What was he doing here? She hadn't expected to see him. She had to swallow twice before she could answer.

'Yes?'

'The band have gone up. You've only got five minutes.'

'Oh...' Her stomach started acting like a washing-machine again.

The bathroom door opened. 'Can I come in?'

'No! Go away! Where's Phil? Where's Diana?' She was feverish, agitated. She couldn't stay still; she was in a state of total witless panic.

'Stop it!' Marc's voice was cool and firm; he caught her, held her, his arms tightly folding her, in spite of her struggles.

'Let go of me! Why isn't Di there? She always stays with me... And Phil... Where are they?' She pushed against his strength, fighting a terrible desire to lean on it.

'They're upstairs, waiting for you. I said I'd bring you up. Here in France you're my star, so I told them I'd look after you until you went on...' His hand smoothed her hair, slowly stroking, caressing, gentling her as if she were a frightened animal.

'I'm used to them,' she said, sulky. 'I need them.'

'No, Annie, you don't,' Marc softly murmured, his mouth against her temples. 'You said it yourself: you're a big girl now; you don't need to have Phil and Di around all the time.'

'I don't need you either!' she said, but she ached to turn her face into his neck. She was quivering at the scent of his skin now, her pulses wild. She remembered the dreams about him being shot, dying, and tears burnt her eyes.

'Don't you, Annie?' he whispered, his hand moving up and down her spine, pressing her closer. 'I need you. As I need air and light and the sky overhead.'

She trembled. 'I had those dreams while I was resting at the hotel,' she whispered. 'Over and over again... Why did you make me start dreaming about it? I never did before, not till I met you. Now I suppose I'll have them for the rest of my life, dreams about something I don't even remember.'

He kissed her eyes, closing them. 'Don't think about them now. You have to go on and sing.'

'I can't!' she wailed, clutching him.

'Of course you can,' he soothed. 'I'll be there. You'll sing for me, Annie. This time you'll be singing for me.'

She heard the possessive note in his voice and her heart clenched in answering emotion.

Marc's mouth searched for her lips. She had stopped fighting it. She gave them up to him, her arms going round his neck, pulling him closer. She had lied. She did need him.

Marc pulled away first, breathing thickly, face darkly flushed.

'Time to go!' he muttered, and led her to the door. Outside in the passage people thronged, watching her, smiling, patting her as she went past for luck, saying it in French or English. She didn't hear a word they said; she just smiled automatically, nodding, her legs moving, one after the other, without her knowing what she was doing, like someone going to the scaffold.

They halted at the edge of the stage, just out of sight. Marc still had his arm round her. Phil came and kissed her, so did Diana, but Marc went on holding her in that possessive grip. She was vaguely aware of the curiosity, surprise, questioning in the looks Phil and Di gave them, but they didn't ask any questions.

Out on the centre of the stage a compere in a glittering red and silver lamé suit was doing a build-up for her. The audience were restless, chanting, 'Annie! Annie! Annie!'

At last the smiling compère gave her cue. 'And here she is now...' There was a long drum roll. 'The lady you've all come to see—here in France, for her first big tour...' Another long drum roll, and cheers. 'So let's hear you; I want to hear you loud and clear... Let's show her how much we love her...that wild and wonderful little-girl-lost...' Another final long drum roll. 'Annie Dumont!'

The crowd erupted into cheers. Marc kissed the top of her head and then pushed her gently forward. Annie automatically began to go through the rehearsed movements, ran out into the black centre of that enormous stage, with that storm of sound deafening her. A blue spot circled her and she stood there in the gesture with which Phil liked her to begin and end each gig—feet apart, arms flung wide, as if to take the whole audience to her heart, hands open, palms up.

The cheers rolled round and round her. She smiled, coming out of the chill daze in which she'd begun.

'*Salut! Ça va?*' she shouted into the microphone.

'*Salut, Annie!*' the audience roared back.

'*C'est formidable de vous voir!*' she told them, easily going into the script Phil had written for her.

By the time she began her first song they were eating out of her hand; she felt them out there, in the dark, barely breathing, giving her all their attention. Her adrenalin was flowing. Her nerves had all gone. She was living on a mountain peak as she finished the song and whirled across the vast stage, the spotlight following her.

The dancers flashed on, glittering in the dark, sequinned and diamond-bright. Annie called out their names, and the audience broke into tumultuous applause. She danced too, then sang again; you could have heard a pin drop as the melancholy notes sighed out. The audience sighed too, before they applauded.

Later, Brick did a long solo, the sound of his drumming rising into the deep blue Paris night sky, and the audience loved that too. Brick was popular. They loved his name, chanted it on and on when he had finished, and he took bow after bow, grinning.

It was a triumphant evening for all of them. Annie sang again and again; the audience would have kept her and the band there forever. Every time they tried to leave, the hoarse, demanding cries broke out again, but at last they left the stage and refused to go back, laughing, flushed, so high that they were almost flying. Champagne corks popped; glasses bubbled over. Everyone was kissing everyone else, but especially Annie. She was hugged so much that she was sure she would be a mass of bruises next day.

Phil and Di were there, lit up, over the moon with excitement. They kissed her, told her she had been marvellous, wonderful, never sung better, sheer magic.

On the far side of the room she saw Marc, his dark eyes fixed and intense.

He didn't come near her, but as their eyes met she felt her whole body shudder.

The noisy, crowded hubbub in the room faded briefly. She remembered the house on the edge of the forest, the silence, the remoteness. She remembered lying in Marc's arms in the darkness under the trees, overwhelmed by an emotion she hadn't expected, didn't understand.

She was used to singing in public, in front of big crowds, used to confusion and screaming fans, the crash and roar of decibels around her. She wasn't used to the way Marc made her feel. It scared her.

'Come on, time you got out of your stage gear and showered. There's a party laid on back at the hotel,' Diana said beside her.

Annie jumped, green eyes wide. 'What?'

'Don't worry, just a few hundred people,' said Di, laughing.

They were always too high after a performance to be able to calm down. Brick was almost walking on the ceiling. He had drumsticks in his hand and kept drumming on people's heads, on tables and chairs and walls. He wasn't drunk or on drugs, just pumped so full of adrenalin that he was crazy.

Usually Annie felt the same. She loved being on stage, performing, giving out. All the energy flowing out of her came back tenfold from the audience. For hours after a gig she couldn't think of anything else. Not tonight. Tonight she couldn't think of anything but Marc.

She took her shower, towelled dry, dressed in a party dress—one of the few she owned, a glittery green and silver thing, with a low neckline and almost no back, thin straps, a tight waist and short flared skirt that showed off her slender legs.

When she emerged again everyone whistled. Brick began singing in his rough, funny voice: one of their own songs, one he'd written. 'She's too sexy to be good... too sexy, that's too bad... Just watch the way she walks...'

Annie threw a cushion at him.

A few minutes later the security men took her and the band out along one of the secret passages, to be smuggled out in another van and taken to their hotel. They were whisked up to another suite, a larger one, already full of people and the throb of recorded music. Annie was handed more champagne, but only sipped it; she didn't need it to take her any higher.

Marc was there, but he never came near her. She kept seeing him, looking at him. He looked back at her, his eyes compelling, dragging her into their depths as if she were being drawn helplessly into a black hole in space.

Then someone would talk to her; she would have to answer, look at them, and Marc would get lost in the crowd again. But Annie had him on her mind all the time. She was throbbing with feeling, a deep, burning sensation inside her, a desire that hurt.

She had sung for him tonight. Not for the audience. For Marc; aware of him all the time, singing to him, for him, all of herself given in the music.

Slowly she began to come down from the elation that had filled her ever since the concert ended. That was when Marc came over to her. She stiffened as she felt him approach. He looked down at her and said quietly, 'Time you were in bed.'

The others protested, yelled, 'Hey! It's still early! Don't break the party up!'

But Annie nodded, her face very pale now. 'I am tired.'

'I'll escort you back to your suite,' Marc said.

She caught Diana's quick, searching look, felt Phil's frowning attention. They didn't say anything, but she knew they were looking from her to Marc and back again, working out what was happening between them. Usually it was one of them who took care of her, and any minute now, no doubt, they had been meaning to tell her to go to bed, just as it would have been one of them who stayed behind with her before the gig and ushered her upstairs on to the stage. Tonight, though, Marc had usurped their usual place, and they were watching her with surprise and no doubt a little alarm.

To reassure them she went and kissed them good-night. 'You two stay at the party, enjoy yourselves. I'm having trouble staying awake.'

She saw from their faces that they wanted to argue, insist on going with her, but with everyone else listening they didn't like to make any sort of scene, so all their questions would have to wait.

Marc didn't say anything as he walked her through the quiet hotel to her suite, but he followed her inside.

She turned on him in a flurry of agitation. 'Good-night, Marc!'

He caught hold of her shoulders and drew her towards him, kissed her possessively, lifted his head and looked down into her flushed, drowsy face.

'You sang for me, didn't you?'

'Yes,' she breathed, staring at his mouth and aching to kiss it again.

He smiled. 'Goodnight, Annie.'

She instinctively, without thinking, stood on tiptoe to meet his mouth as it came down again, but the kiss was brief, gentle, and a moment later Marc was gone, closing the door softly behind him, leaving her dying for him.

Next morning she was nervous as she first saw Di and Phil, but although it was obvious they were longing to ask questions she soon realised that they had decided on a policy of ignoring the subject of Marc. Every time his name came up Annie felt the prickle of awareness in the air, saw Phil and Diana exchange looks, bite back questions. She almost wished they would ask. It might clear the air. But what could she say, if they did? She didn't know herself what was happening.

They had to be moving on to Lyon that afternoon. Nobody got up before noon, and when the band surfaced they were all drained and pale. Even Brick was flat and hardly said a syllable, didn't even tap out a drum roll on his saucer with his spoon as he usually did at mealtimes, just yawned and stared at nothing, giving an occasional groan when he moved too fast or someone spoke too loudly.

The luxuriously fitted coach which was taking them on to Lyon turned up at the hotel at three and they all climbed into it. Brick fell asleep as they left the Paris suburbs behind and headed along the Péage.

There had been no sign of Marc before they left.
Would he turn up in Lyon? wondered Annie, staring out
of the smoked glass of the coach window, lying back in
her reclining chair. As the next hours passed she began
to need to see him. He was in her mind all the time; she
kept closing her eyes and seeing him, daydreaming about
him, remembering what he had said, how he had looked
at her, the touch of his mouth. Minutes dragged; time
was endless. She felt as if it was weeks since she last saw
him.

He appeared just before she was about to go on stage
for the next gig. Annie felt her heart turn over at the
sight of him. She had been feeling tired and depressed,
in no condition to sing up a storm that night, but instantly her mood changed; her adrenalin shot up, her
green eyes brilliant as he smiled at her.

'I'll take her up,' he told Phil and Diana, who were
by then her only companions.

They stirred, faintly resentful, looked at Annie, who
was barely conscious of them, watching Marc with her
heart in her eyes.

Any protest they might have made died on their lips.
They kissed her and went, wishing her luck for the gig.
They were hardly out of the door before she was in
Marc's arms.

'Missed me?'

She didn't bother to answer. He knew. She clung,
kissing him, and Marc sat down on the small couch in
the dressing-room, pulled her on to his lap, and kissed
her again.

Sometimes when they were alone she forgot the darker
side of their relationship: the dreams, the over-
shadowing past, of which Marc was always aware.

The present was all that mattered to Annie: now, this moment, Marc kissing her, holding her.

'Sing for me again tonight, just for me,' he whispered, and she did.

She sang with such passion and attack that she felt the band staring in amazement, and the audience went wild. It was the best gig she had ever done in her life.

Afterwards she was in tears, and everyone hugged her and told her how good she'd been, but she only had eyes for Marc, feeling his response across the room throughout the party afterwards. It was Marc who told her the party was over for her, again. It was Marc who took her back to her suite in the grand Lyon hotel, in the centre, between the Rhone and the Saone.

By then everyone knew about them. The band had begun making jokes, grinned at her, lifted eyebrows, but only if Marc wasn't there, because they were nervous of him; he was formidable, not a man to risk annoying.

Diana finally came out with what had been bothering her and Phil, her face and voice tentative, uncertain. 'Is it serious, Annie? Because...well...he's a lot older than you, and he's...well, French...'

Annie laughed a little wildly. 'What does that mean? Of course he's French; what has that got to do with anything? So am I—well, half French, at least.'

Di looked taken aback, as if that had never registered. 'Yes, I'd forgotten, I suppose you are...but you've never lived here...'

'I'm still half French, and Marc's only ten years older than me. That isn't too big a gap.'

'But with men like him, well, there must have been a lot of other women. He's far too sexy not to have had a busy love-life.'

'I know all about his past,' Annie said with conscious dryness. 'You'd be surprised how much I know about him.' Very surprised! she thought, and a lot more worried.

'You can't be sure he's told you everything!' Diana said, flushed and irritable. 'Annie, you've led a very sheltered life. I can't help wondering if you're up to coping with a man like him!'

'I'm learning,' Annie said, suddenly laughing. 'Di, I'm twenty-four! Time I made my own mistakes. Just let me do that, will you?'

Diana didn't know what to say, worried her lip with her teeth, frowning. 'You're so different suddenly. Ever since we got back from our honeymoon...' She broke off, watching her uneasily. 'You didn't resent it when Phil and I got married, did you?'

Annie had, but that seemed a long, long time ago. It no longer mattered to her at all. She shook her head, smiling at Di. 'I'm glad for both of you; I can see you're happy together, and that's great. It's true it changed things, but I think they had to change, don't you? You and Phil took such good care of me that I was far too comfortable to think of living a life of my own. Now, I can, and I'm discovering all sorts of things about myself.'

Diana looked taken aback, even more unsure, but she managed a smile. 'That's great, Annie, but...oh, do be careful, won't you? Marc Pascal is very sophisticated and experienced—and you're not. We just don't want you to get hurt! Maybe Phil should talk to him, check his background out, make sure he isn't married!'

'He isn't,' Annie said with confidence.

Diana gave her an impatient, almost pitying glance. 'Annie, he may have told you he isn't, but he could be lying. You only just met him; you can't be certain you can trust him. You've known Phil for years; you do know you can trust Phil.'

'Yes,' Annie said slowly, confusion sweeping over her.

'Let Phil find out more about him,' Di coaxed. 'After all, you never know! Men can be very deceptive.'

Annie hesitated, then sighed and nodded. 'OK.' She was used to letting Phil handle all her affairs, and she did trust him. Yet, looking back over the past few weeks, Annie saw how much she had changed since Di and Phil got married, or was it only since she met Marc? she suddenly wondered. How much influence had he had on her?

'Don't let him split you off from us!' Diana pleaded. 'You've been with Phil all these years, since you were a total beginner—it doesn't seem very fair to let a total stranger come between you and Phil now that you're a big star, does it?'

'I wouldn't,' Annie said, but uncertainly, because Marc was coming between her and Phil now, and she knew it.

'He's trying to,' said Di shortly. 'He's no fool, is he? If you become a big international star, you could make millions. As soon as he met you he wanted a piece of that, I've no doubt.'

'No, he isn't like that!' protested Annie, but she wondered, in her heart—was he? What did she really know about him, after all?

'You can't be sure of that, can you?' said Di, and it was true. She couldn't be sure of Marc; she had only known him such a short time. How did she even know that his tales about remembering his past life, and having

known her before, were anything but fairy-tales? Was
Diana right? Was he only really interested in the money
she would be making in the future, in the powerful role
of star-maker to one of today's big names? He was un-
questionably trying to take her over, acting possessively,
always there when she looked round, waiting for his
moment to move in and snatch her away from the others,
make it clear that she belonged to him now.

'Keep him at a distance until Phil has checked him
out,' Di begged, and she bit her lip, then nodded
reluctantly.

'OK. Now we're moving on out of France, I doubt if
I'll be seeing much of him anyway.'

Phil made a few phone calls at once, and came back
to shrug and say, 'Well, so far he checks out OK. There
don't seem to be any skeletons in his cupboard, but we'll
dig deeper, and see what we come up with.'

'You won't come up with anything,' Annie said defiantly, crossing her fingers behind her back in a childish
gesture.

'Don't get too serious about him, Annie,' pleaded Phil.
'Wait until we know more about him.'

After the gig at Lyon they were due to drive over the
border into Switzerland and on to Germany, where they
were to play at several venues, but that afternoon, just
before they were all to board the coach, Marc arrived
in a red Ferrari, roaring up while the band admiringly
coveted the sleek sports car.

'D'you think he'd sell it to me?' Brick asked her. 'Hey,
ask him if I can take it for a quick spin. I'd give my
drumsticks to get my hands on that steering-wheel.'

She told Marc, who laughed, shaking his head, telling
her in quick, dry French, 'I never let anyone drive this

car, and certainly not a twenty-year-old kid who has already smashed up a couple of his own cars!'

'Brick is reckless,' she had to admit, and turned to tell Brick he couldn't drive the Ferrari.

'Selfish swine!' Brick yelled at Marc, who grinned.

'I'm probably saving your life. She's a killer.'

That just excited Brick even more. 'I love dangerous cars and dangerous women,' he moaned as his friends dragged him on to the coach.

'So do I,' Marc said softly, looking down at Annie.

Flushed and uneasy, remembering what she had promised Diana, she said, 'I'd better board the coach, too.'

'You aren't going with them,' he informed her. 'You're coming with me.'

She stiffened, shook her head, her black hair loose around her face. 'I'm sorry, Marc, I can't come with you. I have to go with the band. They would be hurt if I didn't. They'd sulk for days. They expect me to travel with them, not go waltzing off alone, as if I'm special, and they're just the hired help!'

His face was tight, determined. 'You can travel with them for the rest of the tour, but just for a couple of days I want you with me. You aren't due to start rehearsing for your next gig until Wednesday; that gives us plenty of time.'

'What for?' she asked, agitated.

His arm went round her and he urged her into the passenger seat of the Ferrari. She resisted. 'Marc, I can't... My luggage is on the coach...and Phil and Diana will wonder what on earth has happened to me!'

They had gone on ahead some hours ago to make sure that everything was OK at the other end—that the hotels had rooms ready, and the stage and seating was well under way.

'The band can tell them you're with me.' Marc had got her into the car; he closed the door, turned, and called to Brick and the others, 'I'm taking Annie with me; we'll join you all in good time to do the gig.'

'Hey, what do you mean? What's going on?' Brick shouted, looking alarmed.

Marc jumped into the Ferrari and turned the ignition key; the car gave a dramatic roar, and as Brick came running towards them the Ferrari shot away.

'Buckle your seatbelt!' Marc tersely told her as she stared helplessly back at Brick's angry face.

'Where are you taking me?' she asked shakily, suddenly realising that they were alone again. What was he planning? Was Diana right about him? Was he ambitious, scheming, a clever man who had seen the way to get control of a coming big name? What did he have in mind for her now?

'The Jura,' he said, and her lips parted in a silent gasp. Marc shot her a look as they fed into the horrendous traffic passing through Lyon's choked and crowded motorways. 'I'm surprised you didn't guess!' he murmured, and of course she should have done. She might have done, in fact, if she hadn't been distracted by Diana's defensive worry about Marc and his possible threat to Phil's management of her career.

'But . . . isn't it hundreds of miles away?' she huskily asked.

'You have no sense of direction, do you?' Marc was drily amused. 'No, Annie, it isn't that far from here to the Jura. We should get there by this evening, in time for dinner. I've booked into a small local auberge I know,

near my village. They do great food, regional special-
ties; it's a simple place, but comfortable, and the people
are kind.'

'Are you taking me to meet your family?' Her heart
was beating suffocatingly fast. He had to be serious if
he was taking her home, and, even more important, obviously Diana was wrong: he wasn't married, or he
wouldn't risk introducing her to his family.

'Tomorrow,' he promised. 'You'll love them, and I
know they're going to love you. Don't look so worried.
You're tired; you haven't caught up with your sleep yet.
Lie back and close your eyes; rest for a while.'

She didn't argue. She was too surprised, for one thing,
and, for another, it was true. She was very tired; she
had used up so much energy over the last week, and had
little real rest. She shut her eyes and leaned back in the
seat, letting her mind drift. She was going to the Jura.

Home, she thought, with a start of surprise. I'm going
home. She had never really had a home since she was
eleven and her father died. From that moment on she
had been very conscious of being alone in the world.
Her mother had never loved her; she had never felt she
belonged, and everyone had a deep need to find a place
in which they belonged.

Maybe she would find she belonged in Jura.

She slept, and dreamed of green forests and green
valleys, crisp, cool air, wild flowers in every pasture,
below every stone wall, the sound of church bells ringing
across the miles, climbing peaks of blue-hazed foothills
with behind them white-capped mountain ranges. It
wouldn't be strange to her, this place she had never visited
before—her father had talked about it when she was very
small, Marc had told her all about it during those hours

alone together, and she had seen it in dreams many times before. She knew it was going to be totally familiar to her when she saw it in her waking hours too.

As they began to climb towards the Swiss border the air grew colder; the sky was blue and as clear as crystal. Annie was grateful for Marc's spare sweater, which he unearthed from a case in his car.

'I've got spare pyjamas, too, for you to borrow,' he said. 'We'll buy you a toothbrush.'

'You should have let me get my case off the coach.'

'You wouldn't have come with me if I'd given you time to think!'

She gave him a wry look. 'Why are men always so bossy?' Then she sighed. 'Phil and Diana are going to be very anxious.'

'They resent me,' he said drily.

'Well, they don't know much about you!'

'They're afraid I may take you away from them.'

She couldn't deny that, startled by his perception. He had got on to that quickly.

He gave her a long, dark-eyed stare, his mouth crooked. 'And I will,' he said, sending a tremor through her. His desire excited her. Yet Phil and Diana's warnings sounded inside her, too. Did he want her because he loved her, or because she was going to be a big star very soon, if Phil's assurances came true?

It was still daylight as they reached the edge of the village of St Jean-des-Pins. Marc slowed as they passed a small, gabled white-painted auberge with a swinging sign showing a silver fish among green reeds. The name 'Auberge des Pêcheurs' was printed in curly red letters below the picture.

'That's where we'll be staying,' Marc said. 'A lot of anglers come up here to fish our rivers, and people heading for the Swiss lakes often stop off for the night, too.' He drove on along a straight, seemingly endless road, running through pine forest, with dark rows of trees on either side.

'Where are we going?' Annie asked nervously, peering into the shadows beneath the pines. 'It will get dark soon.' The light was falling fast; inside the forest it seemed to be as black as night already.

Marc drew off the road and began driving along a narrow, unmade track with trees very close.

'No!' Annie said, suddenly panic-stricken. She knew this track; she knew where they were going. 'I can't! Marc, don't take me there; don't make me go!'

His hand slid sideways, gripped hers. 'Don't be frightened, *chérie*. I'm here; I'll take care of you.'

She reached for the door-handle and struggled to get out. He stopped the car. She opened the door and jumped down, and Marc leapt out too and ran round to grab her, his arms going round her.

'Why are you so scared? There's nothing there now,' he soothed.

'You know it's there,' Annie babbled, fevered and trembling. 'I've dreamt about it... I know it will be worse when I'm actually there, where it happened. It will be too much. I can't bear it.'

Marc held on to her, his face against her windblown black hair. 'Listen, Annie, listen to the forest...'

It breathed all round them, stirring in the wind, rustling, hissing like boiling water, crackling as twigs snapped and fell. It was never still.

She was fascinated, terrified.

'Trust me,' Marc pleaded. 'All I want you to do is walk up that track over there...'

'To the hut,' she broke out, shaking. 'I know where it goes. It will be dark in there... I hate dreaming about it... There's such a bad feeling about it. It's empty; he's gone, gone forever.' That sense of terrible loss came over her again, as it had in her dreams.

'I'm here,' Marc whispered, kissing her cheek, and she felt time dislocate again, swerve back into the present. Dazedly she looked up at him, put her arms around him, as if he might be snatched away from her again.

'Oh, Marc! What's happening to me? I'm terrified. Am I going mad? I can't go up there. I don't need to go; I know what it looks like.'

'I want you to see,' he insisted gently. 'You must see with your own eyes that it's all true.'

She hesitated, shivering in the wind, then sighed and gave in. He was right. She had to see, with her own eyes. She had to know.

The walk was a steep climb, in growing darkness. Annie jumped at every sound, kept looking round, eyes dilated. When she saw the hut she stopped in her tracks, her heart turning over and over.

'It's...exactly as I remember...saw it...' In those dreams, she thought. She had only seen it in dreams, and who was to say that Marc hadn't somehow managed to make her dream like that?

But could he make her remember like this? So vividly? Because she knew this place as if she had seen it all her life. She recognised every detail: the way the logs were piled around the outside, under the overhang of the wood-tiled roof; the door; the shuttered window; a covered wooden water barrel; the clearing around the hut; the pine trees stretching endlessly on either side; and even an old mountain ash growing near by, with new green leaves showing on the creaking old boughs.

Annie looked at the hut door, shuddering.

'I can't go inside! Don't try to make me!'

'Even with me?'

Annie looked up at him, into his deep, dark eyes, gave a long sigh. 'Oh, if I must...' With Marc beside her she felt she could face anything.

'Now where's the key hidden?' Marc said, and without needing to think Annie replied.

'Under the doorstep.'

Then she froze, turning white. How had she known that?

Marc was breathing audibly. Without looking at her, he bent down and felt slowly along the under-edge of the wooden doorstep, straightened with a key in his hand.

Neither of them said a word. He put the key in the door and there was a metallic grating, then Marc pushed the door open.

Annie stood on the threshold, stiff and tense, looking inside. The air was damp and cold, smelling of earth. There was an old wooden chair, a fixed wooden platform bed in one corner, on which a straw palliasse might be spread, a rusty old stove in the centre of the hut, with a round chimney going up into the roof, a shelf with a few mugs, plates, a saucepan hanging from a nail and another pile of logs along the wall, kept dry out of the wind and rain.

Nothing had changed. She recognised it all. Instantly. Even the saucepan hanging there in the same place, the old, battered tin plates once painted white with a blue rim, all so familiar that she might have seen them yesterday.

Tears came into her eyes. She turned her face into the wooden wall and leaned there, shuddering, overwhelmed with a rush of memory which was like being in a speeding train and seeing fields, stations, people, flash past. Faster and faster they came, faces looming out of the mist of time, scenes, images.

'Oh, no, oh, no,' she kept saying.

Marc stood closely behind her, holding her. 'Ssh...darling, don't...don't cry; we'll go, if it's going to upset you like this!'

She didn't even hear him. She was somewhere else, back in the past, in his arms, not here, in this hut, but out in the forest, under the trees, on a warm summer night, making love on a bed of ferns which rustled every time they moved, the fresh scent of the crushed leaves and grass so strong that Annie could smell it now. She had her eyes shut, breathing in that scent, which brought with it all the intensity of pleasure she had felt in his arms. Her hands moved with tactile sensuality over his skin, his broad shoulders and the long, deep indentation of his spine, feeling the power of his body at her fingertips, hearing the rough torture of his breathing as he moved on top of her. She held him closer, pulling him down into her, wanting to hold him like that forever.

Moonlight dappled their pale bodies, rippled over them like silent water. Knowing the danger they were in gave a deeper, wilder note to their cries of pleasure. They made love with desperation, a hunger that could never be satisfied, always aware that it might be for the last time. In an uncertain world only love had meaning, but love was so fragile and death was always just around the corner. They couldn't have enough of each other.

Suddenly the image changed, startling her, like a blow in the face. She gave a low moan, doubling up in pain. Somehow she knew that this was the very next time she had seen him. A day later. When he was brought down to the village by his killers, who were demanding that he be identified, threatening reprisals, wanting to know who had been sheltering him, accusing the villagers. Annie had stood in the doorway of her shop, had seen him carried past: white, horribly rigid, dappled now with dry, blackening blood.

She couldn't bear any more. She dragged herself back to the present, to the hut, sobbing, shaking.

'Oh, why did you make me come here?' she muttered to Marc. 'I don't want to remember... It hurts too much.'

'It was all a long time ago, Annie. It can't hurt us now,' he said softly, his hand stroking rhythmically over her hair and down her back. 'Tell me what you just remembered... You did remember something, didn't you?'

She was silent for a moment, then she whispered shakily, 'We came back here, after making love in the forest that last time. We came back here, to the hut...'

She felt him listening, everything in him intent on her and what she was telling him. His hand soothed, comforted her, the warmth of it seeping into her chilled body.

'You said you wished we could have had a child,' she remembered, and at once saw it all again, playing in her head, saw his face, heard his voice, wanted to weep because he was dead. But he wasn't. He was here, listening to her. Confusion made her head swim. She shook her head, stumbling on, 'But you said we shouldn't...things

being the way they were; it would have made my life a
misery in the village... Country people have such fixed
ideas; they'd never have forgiven me. You said you
wouldn't do that to me. If we both survived the war,
you said, you would come back and find me, and we
would get married, but in case we didn't survive, never
met again, you said we mustn't just go out like a candle-
flame and leave nothing behind, as if we'd never been
here at all.'

She stiffened at that instant, went dead white, gave a
gasp.

'What?' Marc asked quickly, at once aware of a change
in her.

Annie looked up at him, turned, looked round the
hut, biting her lip. Marc waited, his face pale and tense.

'What is it, Annie?'

Annie stared at the piles of logs near the window.
'Over there... It was over there...' She began pulling
the logs aside to expose the wall behind them, and after
a brief pause Marc came to help her. It was hard, dirty
work, but Annie hardly noticed the effort she had to
make.

Five minutes later she stopped dead, breathing
hoarsely. She fell on her knees and put out a shaking
hand to touch deeply cut initials which had been carved
into the lowest board of the hut wall. They had faded
now, but could still be clearly read: the first letters of
their names, A and M, entwined, and underneath the
word FOREVER. The passing of half a century had not
wiped them out. Forever, she thought. Was that why
they had both come back? Had they somehow reached
into eternity with the intensity of their feeling?

Marc knelt down beside her and touched the letters too, with a fingertip, staring at them.

'Oh, Marc...' she breathed, turning to look at him. 'They're still here.'

He looked into her eyes, his eyes glowing. 'So are we, Annie.' He was breathing very fast, his skin darkly flushed. 'I love you,' he said in a deep voice roughened by feeling, then his mouth was on hers, hot and insistent.

Any doubts she had ever had were gone. She knew with utter certainty that she loved this man once long ago, loved him now, just as she had loved him before, in another life and time. They had been cheated of that love last time; death had snatched him away. But they had another chance now.

Marc reluctantly lifted his mouth, stared down at her passionate face. '*Chérie*...' he whispered. 'I've loved you for so long. I knew I'd find you again one day, from the moment I began remembering. And ever since I saw that photo of you and recognised you, I only had one idea in my head—finding you again. I'd have come to find you at once, but I had to wait and plan it. I was afraid you would think I was crazy...'

'I did,' she said, half smiling, half sighing.

'But you believe me now...' His eyes were brilliant with assurance and belief.

'I've been remembering bits on and off ever since we met,' she confessed. 'I didn't want to... I thought I might be going mad, too, but just now it was all so vivid and real that I knew it wasn't just imagination. I was re-membering something that had really happened...'

'I knew you would; you had to,' he said huskily. 'What we remember are bits of eternity. They come and go. Some things are clear, others aren't, but one thing I'm certain about: we belong together. We've been given our chance to make a life together, to have the children we never had before.' He broke off, gave her a quick, frowning look.

'What is it?' asked Annie, at once alert.

'I couldn't live anywhere but France, Annie,' he said abruptly. 'How do you feel about that? I suppose we could compromise, live six months here, six months in England...but...'

'I'll be happy living in Paris,' she said, her eyes brilliant with feeling. 'Have you forgotten I'm half French? And wherever you are is my home. We'll work something out with Phil and Di—there's no reason why he shouldn't go on being my manager, is there?'

'None at all,' said Marc. 'I have my own business to run. Phil's OK; I like him. I'm sure we can come to a friendly agreement. We'll make it work, don't worry, Annie, my love.' He caressed her cheek with his mouth, kissed her lashes and lids, whispered, 'All that matters is that we're together.'

She pulled him closer, began kissing him again. She could have stayed there in the cold little hut forever, kissing him, their bodies warm and breathing in that close embrace, but Marc pulled back, sighing deeply, after a long moment.

'It's getting late; it's pitch-black out there. We'd better get going, back to the auberge.'

He helped her up and they left the hut, their arms around each other. Marc smiled at her, his face glowing with the same joy she felt.

'Tonight we'll have dinner together, and talk, talk about everything, Annie. I want to know just what you remember. Then in the morning I'll take you to meet my family, and tell them that I've met the woman I have been waiting for all my life, that I am going to marry her—as soon as she has said yes!'

'Yes,' Annie said.

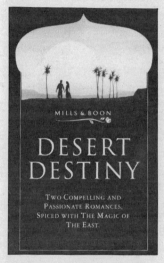
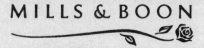

Next Month's Romances

Each month you can choose from a wide variety of romance with Mills & Boon. Below are the new titles to look out for next month, why not ask either Mills & Boon Reader Service or your Newsagent to reserve you a copy of the titles you want to buy – just tick the titles you would like and either post to Reader Service or take it to any Newsagent and ask them to order your books.

Please save me the following titles: Please tick | ✓

Title	Author	
NO RISKS, NO PRIZES	Emma Darcy	
ANGEL OF DARKNESS	Lynne Graham	
BRITTLE BONDAGE	Anne Mather	
SENSE OF DESTINY	Patricia Wilson	
THE SUN AT MIDNIGHT	Sandra Field	
DUEL IN THE SUN	Sally Wentworth	
MYTHS OF THE MOON	Rosalie Ash	
MORE THAN LOVERS	Natalie Fox	
LEONIE'S LUCK	Emma Goldrick	
WILD INJUSTICE	Margaret Mayo	
A MAGICAL AFFAIR	Victoria Gordon	
SPANISH NIGHTS	Jennifer Taylor	
FORSAKING ALL REASON	Jenny Cartwright	
SECRET SURRENDER	Laura Martin	
SHADOWS OF YESTERDAY	Cathy Williams	
BOTH OF THEM	Rebecca Winters	

If you would like to order these books in addition to your regular subscription from Mills & Boon Reader Service please send £1.90 per title to: Mills & Boon Reader Service, Freepost, P.O. Box 236, Croydon, Surrey, CR9 9EL, quote your Subscriber No:................................... (if applicable) and complete the name and address details below. Alternatively, these books are available from many local Newsagents including W H Smith, J Menzies, Martins and other paperback stockists from 9 September 1994.

Name:...

Address:...

....Post Code:........................

To Retailer: If you would like to stock M&B books please contact your regular book/magazine wholesaler for details.

You may be mailed with offers from other reputable companies as a result of this application.
If you would rather not take advantage of these opportunities please tick box. ☐

Accept 4 FREE Romances and 2 FREE gifts

FROM READER SERVICE

Here's an irresistible invitation from Mills & Boon. Please accept our offer of 4 FREE Romances, a CUDDLY TEDDY and a special MYSTERY GIFT! Then, if you choose, go on to enjoy 6 captivating Romances every month for just £1.90 each, postage and packing FREE. Plus our FREE Newsletter with author news, competitions and much more.

Send the coupon below to: Mills & Boon Reader Service, FREEPOST, PO Box 236, Croydon, Surrey CR9 9EL.

- - - ┤ NO STAMP REQUIRED ├ - - - - - - - - - - - - - - - - -

Yes! Please rush me 4 FREE Romances and 2 FREE gifts! Please also reserve me a Reader Service subscription. If I decide to subscribe I can look forward to receiving 6 brand new Romances for just £11.40 each month, post and packing FREE. If I decide not to subscribe I shall write to you within 10 days - I can keep the free books and gifts whatever I choose. I may cancel or suspend my subscription at any time. I am over 18 years of age.

Ms/Mrs/Miss/Mr _____   EP70R

Address _____

_____

Postcode _____ Signature _____